Value Stream Mapping in the OR

Gerard Leone
Richard D. Rahn

Flow Publishing Inc.
Boulder, Colorado

**Value Stream Mapping in the OR
by Gerard Leone and Richard D. Rahn**

Illustrations by Catherine L. Rahn

Published by:

Flow Publishing Inc.
7690 Watonga Way
Boulder, Colorado 80303
(303) 494-4693
www.flowpublishing.com
contact@flowpublishing.com

ISBN-13   978-0-9833839-4-9

Table of Contents

4 Value Stream Mapping in the OR

Introduction to Value Stream Mapping

Value Stream Mapping (VSM) is an assessment tool that can be used in hospitals to assemble a plan of continuous improvement for a department, section, area, or the entire hospital. While creating a flow chart is not a new technique, VSM was developed in the 1990's in manufacturing as a way of shining a spotlight on workflow from a Lean perspective, using a body of specific symbols to represent Lean methods. Let's start with some definitions of VSM.

Value Stream Mapping I

A technique used to analyze the flow of materials and information required to bring a product or service to a customer.

Value Stream Mapping II

A visual documentation of the actions required to bring a product through the main flows essential to every product.

Value Stream Mapping III – Our Favorite

A graphical display of the relationship of processes required to complete one unit of value.

A simple way to look at a value stream map is as a flow chart that documents the work steps that a unit of value goes through, from start to finish. Let's dissect this definition by its elements.

Process – The How

A *process* is a collection of sequential steps of like work required to advance the value towards its point of completion. A *task* is the smallest element of work in a process. Tasks are documented in work instructions call *standard work definitions*. Here's the logical hierarchy: hospital work is made of value streams. A *value stream* is made up of processes. A process is made up of tasks.

A process really means *work*. You know it when you see it: work that is performed by a person (OR Nurse), a machine (Autoclave), or a combination of people and machines (Imaging Tech with C-Arm).

Value – The What

The reason why the value stream exists is to deliver *value* to someone.

Notice how we avoid the use of the term *product* when discussing hospital value streams. In a hospital the product may be a patient, but a patient is *not* a product. Using the term product within the context of patient care is ill-advised.

Why Value Stream Mapping

The value stream mapping technique is not a panacea that will solve all problems, but it is our tool of choice for launching a Lean Hospital initiative. The main reasons to use VSM are:

To Assess Current Performance. By identifying the process relationships, the process times, and the delays between processes, you will have a picture of the elapsed time to move the value from the start to the finish of the value stream, compared to the work time applied to the value. The difference can be staggering. From the time a patient walks in to register for an elective procedure until the time the patient is discharged home from Phase II, he/she is receiving medical attention less than 20% of the time. From the time a used instrument set is placed back onto the case cart until the time that the instrument set is available for use again, it may be waiting to be worked on 90% of the time. One of the metrics you will measure as you develop your value stream maps is the ratio of time the value is being worked on, *value adding time*, versus the time the value is waiting, *non-value adding time*.

To Identify Sources of Waste: Waste is defined as all work that does not advance the value towards its point of completion. Waste is work that adds cost but does not add value. A term very commonly used is non-value adding work. This work may be required and it may be unavoidable, but if it does not add value it is waste. If a nurse needs to help a patient off a bed and needs a lift, the value-adding work is the use of the lifting device to help the patient. The time that the nurse spent hunting for the lift is waste. The nine types of waste will be described in more detail in Chapter Nine.

To Brainstorm Opportunities for Improvement. This is the main reason why we recommend using the VSM method. We like to call it the *campfire effect*. While you are developing a VSM with a team, you are all huddled around the same campfire, and all the elements of the VSM will be documented by consensus, and by physically visiting the processes to confirm every statement made. By working as a team, you will take advantage of multiple brains on the case. This is another example of the power of Lean. VSM is not for the *selected few* experts drawing charts in a conference room and instructing you how to do your job. The VSM team is a group of staff members that work in the processes like SPD, OR or PACU every day and know exactly where it hurts.

To Estimate Future Performance. At the conclusion of a value stream mapping project, you will develop a *future state value stream map* that incorporates *all* of the proposed improvements. That will give you a new

picture of the total lead-time, the ratio of value
-adding to non-value-adding time, and a vision
of what is possible.

To Serve as a Master Plan: A value stream
map points the team in the direction of
continuous improvement. To get the most out
of a VSM couple it with three simple tools from
the *goal deployment* method:

The *A3 X-Chart*. This simple matrix displays
the relationships between the hospital's goals,
the projects identified, the metrics tracked, the
expected benefits, and the responsible staff
members.

The *A3 Team Charter*. This is a kaizen event
planning form, with sections for the issue
statement, target statement, analysis, proposed
action, implementation plan, and audit.

The *A3 Team Status Report*. This form is used
to report on the progress of an improvement
project, and can be requested periodically by
OR leadership or a Lean steering committee.

Global Steps in Value Stream Mapping

There are three main steps that you will follow when
developing a VSM:

1. Create a *current state value stream map*. This is
    the first step, completely documenting the value
    stream as it is today, warts and all.

2. *Brainstorm Improvements.* Once you have created a picture of the current state, you will dissect it using your experience and knowledge of the processes, in search for ways to improve them. The result will be a lengthy list of opportunities for improvement, so be organized and document them all as you go.

3. Develop the *future state value stream map*. This is a flowchart that shows how the value stream would look if the improvement ideas identified by the VSM team were implemented.

From these three global steps, you must make these suggestions a reality by using a detailed roadmap and creating an implementation plan. A roadmap is a flowchart that depicts a set of proven steps to reach a goal. In this book, for example, we will be describing the roadmap for value stream mapping. Many other roadmaps have been developed by the authors and they are the subject of other books in this series. The upcoming chapters will follow the phases in the roadmap. We will be using an actual OR value stream project, the re-processing of surgical instrument sets, as the example in this book.

It is important to remember that the VSM method is a high-level view of the process relationships. Think about surveying the terrain in an airplane from 30,000 feet. If you fly too high you will not be able to see the contours of the land you are surveying. If you fly too low you might get stuck in the trees of excessive detail.

You can download an annotated version of the value stream mapping roadmap at the Flow Publishing website, under the listing for this book.

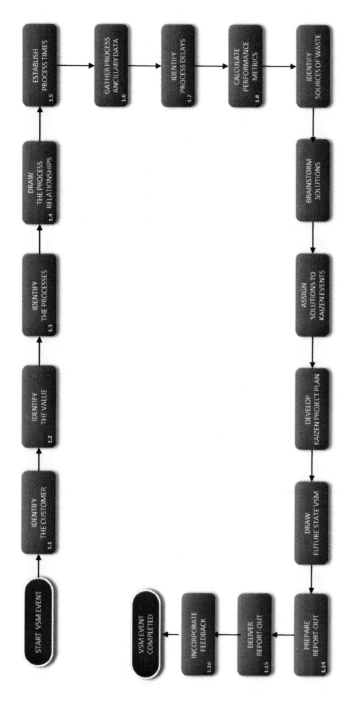

START VSM EVENT

IDENTIFY
THE CUSTOMER
1.1

IDENTIFY
THE VALUE
1.2

IDENTIFY
THE PROCESSES
1.3

DRAW
THE PROCESS
RELATIONSHIPS
1.4

ESTABLISH
PROCESS TIMES
1.5

GATHER PROCESS
ANCILLARY DATA
1.6

IDENTIFY
PROCESS DELAYS
1.7

CALCULATE
PERFORMANCE
METRICS
1.8

IDENTIFY
SOURCES OF WASTE

BRAINSTORM
SOLUTIONS

ASSIGN
SOLUTIONS TO
KAIZEN EVENTS

DEVELOP
KAIZEN PROJECT PLAN

DRAW
FUTURE STATE VSM

PREPARE
REPORT-OUT
1.14

DELIVER
REPORT-OUT
1.15

INCORPORATE
FEEDBACK
1.16

VSM EVENT
COMPLETED

Value Stream Mapping Roadmap. This book will be following the step-by-step process for creating a value stream map, as defined by the VSM roadmap shown here. Download a high-res PDF at www.flowpublishing.com.

Chapter 1: Identify the Customer

The customer is the one that receives the value being created by the value stream within the hospital. Logically in  many cases the customer is the hospital patient, but that is not always the case. Who the customer is depends on the point of view taken for the analysis of the value stream, as well as the boundaries placed on the processes involved. Let's take a look at some examples to clarify what is meant by *the customer*:

> Value Stream: Sterilization of Instruments Sets
>> The Patient?
>> The Surgeon?

> Value Stream: Medication Administration
>> The Patient?
>> The Nurse?

> Value Stream: Replenishment of Medical Supplies
>> The Patient?
>> The Surgeon?
>> The Nurse?
>> The OR Tech?

The tendency is to think that the recipient of value is always the patient, but many other people benefit from the creation and delivery of value throughout the many value streams in the hospital. Ultimately you should consider the patient and his/her family at the center of every action you take. We are, however, not discussing patient care models in this book, but a tool to help you improve how you deliver that care.

Let's start with our sample value stream, and examine the reprocessing of instrument sets for the OR. At the end of this value stream, who is waiting for the instrument set? At the very least, the OR tech and the OR nurse are waiting for the set for use in the OR suite changeover. You also need to consider the surgeon, and the surgeon's assistant. These examples may or may not cover the situation in your department. You need to physically go to the end of the value stream, as defined by you, and verify who the customer is.

It is necessary to identify the customer because only the customer can tell you what is of value to them. We can tell you from experience that on more than one occasion, what we presumed to be the value turned out to be wrong. Only the customer knows what is of value to them. Is speed the overriding value above all? That could lead you in the direction of increasing the number of sets that you flash. Is that a desirable outcome? Is never having an instrument substitution the number one goal? That would drive you in the direction of very long turn times for the instrument sets. You will be best served by going to where the customers are and asking them.

Some practitioners like defining the customer as *the person willing to pay for the value*. That definition works better in retail or manufacturing, where you are discussing purchased products. It does not apply as well in healthcare without a number of provisos, caveats, and further explanations.

Do not wrack your brain wondering about the customer in the current state versus the customer in the future state. It is very likely that the customer will not change. All that will change is your ability to deliver the same value to the same customer with less waste along the value stream.

We now need to introduce some basic features of a value stream map. As we said in the introduction, you are drawing a flowchart. This flowchart shows the flow of the value from a starting point, located on the upper left-hand side of the chart to the end point, located on the upper right-hand side the chart. The flow of the value will be shown across the bottom of the chart. We will come back to this topic a few more times to help you draw a complete value stream map.

You are now ready to take the first step in drawing your value stream map. It will look a bit bare at first, but you have to start somewhere. Draw the customer on the upper right-hand side of the chart. If there is more than one customer, document them all in your notes. It is fine to just document a representative customer in the value stream map itself.

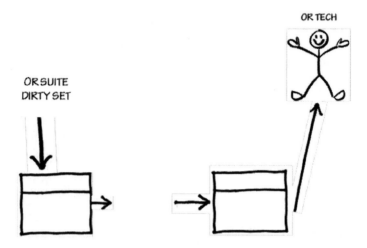

We are showing the OR tech as the customer and we are also displaying the "dirty set" as the value coming from the OR suite from a previous procedure. The two rectangles are called process boxes and they are the graphical representation of the work processes, the subject of the next chapter. The space between the two process boxes above will eventually be filled with all of the process boxes in the value stream.

As Steve Jobs would have said, "Ah...just one more thing." At the end of each chapter you will have the opportunity to check your knowledge, to see if the information in the chapter is sticking.

Chapter 1 Knowledge Check

Why is it important to identify the customer for a specific value stream?

☐ The customer will be paying for the value stream mapping project.

☐ Because the authors of *Value Stream Mapping in the OR* say so.

☐ Because the customer defines the actual value that you will be mapping.

Match the information in column 1 with its physical location on a value stream map in column 2.

Customer	Bottom
Flow of value	Upper right-hand
Starting point	Upper left-hand

True or False: A common rule of thumb to identify the customer is to look for the person willing to *pay for the value.*

☐ True
☐ False

18 Value Stream Mapping in the OR

Chapter 2: Identify the Value

In the prior chapter you went to the end of the value stream to identify the customer. We defined the customer as 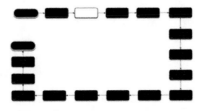 the recipient of the value being created by the value stream's processes. You now need to go back to the value stream and make a positive identification of the value created and delivered by the value stream. Here again, we find ourselves in a bit of a unique situation in a hospital.

Let's take a quick detour and go in your mind to a place that makes travel coffee mugs. What is the value? Easy answer. Take that travel mug to your local coffee shop and ask for your usual triple-grande, no-foam, soy, half-caff, two-splenda mocachino with a cinnamon sprinkle. What is the value there? Easy answer again, even though you could add a twist to the definition of value at the coffee shop by adding service elements like remembering your name, remembering your drink (good luck with that one...), and the overall friendly attitude. Take a sip of that devilish libation and... ouch, my chest! No, it has nothing to do with the coffee. It must be a cramp from that hard game of Jai Alai you played yesterday night against that CCU nurse that seemed to have endless energy. Another sip and... ouch again! That is when you remember that you work in a hospital and you know about this stuff. You know what to do, and you call an ambulance.

You are now at the hospital in the middle of a cardiac alert. You spend some time in the ED and are taken to the Cath Lab. You will then be admitted to the Telemetry Unit and stay for three days. Finally, you are discharged home recovered, properly educated, and ready to face the world again.

Warning: a dogmatic approach is to consider the entire chain of events from your ambulance ride to your discharge home as one value stream. Cosmetically correct as that may be, it does not help you by looking at it in this way. Here is a better way to break down the experience.

Value Stream	Value Delivered	Customer
Ambulance Ride	Sick Patient to ED	ED RN, ED MD, Patient, Family
ED Treatment	Sick Patient to Cath Lab	CCL Tech, CCL RN, Cardiologist, Patient, Family
Hospital Stay	Recovered Patient Home	Patient, Family

You stand to gain nothing from the dogma *the value stream is always door-to-door*, while you stand to gain a lot of benefit from learning, through practice, to define a value stream as *the set of processes that delivers a specific value to a specific customer*. One of our clients was able to reduce their door-to-balloon time by 4.1 minutes by looking at the transportation from ED to the Cath Lab as a value stream. They asked one of our team members, "Is this definition of a value stream correct?" He answered just as he should have, "Who cares? As long as you have a definite start, a definite end, you have processes, you can identify the customer and the value delivered, then you have a value stream."

We are not done yet. Let's pick one of the value streams we defined for you in the table above, the patient's stay in the Tele Unit. This value stream has a definite start (admission), a definite end (discharge), a customer (patient, family), value (recovered patient home). Do you see any other value streams? Take a few seconds, take a deep breath and go on reading.

What about the delivery of medications to the patient? Can you identify the clear start point (script), the clear end point (meds administered to patient), the processes (profiling, picking, checking, delivering, the customer, and finally the value (the five rights)?

Let's try one more. While you are recovering in the Tele unit, you are likely to undergo a series of studies. You could look at each one as a value stream with the definite value being the patient having successfully undergone the exam. The same goes for procedures.

One approach that seems to work very well when you are just getting started with value stream analysis for a department is to get your team together and review everything the department does. You may end up with a very long list and feel a bit confused. Not to worry. Keep building that list of things the department does. You may have a list of all the forms of value delivered by that that department. One example is to look into the pharmacy department. This may have started because you think there is something the pharmacy could do better but you are not sure what. All you know is that stat meds take a long time, a pharmacist is rarely available to consult, and that they must be double or triple checking the meds by the time you get them.

So you volunteer to help the pharmacy with value stream analysis. You get your team together and methodically launch the value stream analysis. You have identified the customer, and now you are looking for the value. In order to avoid rushing to judgment, you ask: So what do you guys do? The answers come back something like this:

- Medication delivery via tube.
- Medication delivery via Pyxis.
- Medication hand delivered (to the patient bin or to the refrigerator).
- Codes.
- Consults with MDs.
- Education to caregivers.
- Education to patients.
- Outpatient prescriptions.
- In-service sessions.

That is just a portion of the list! So what do you do? A very good path to follow is to *analyze the volumes* for these services. You are likely to find one or two options that account for the majority of the volume, the famous 80/20 rule. That is a very good place to start. It may not be a good place to end, though, as there may be a lower volume service that causes most of the pain, and which cannot be ignored.

With the customer and the value defined, your incipient value stream map drawn in Chapter 1 remains the same, still very blank in the middle.

Chapter 2 Knowledge Check

True or False: In a hospital setting, the value that is delivered through a value stream is always *medical procedures.*

☐ True
☐ False

The value that is being delivered in a value stream map is ultimately determined by:

☐ The VSM Project Team.
☐ The AORN Standards Manual.
☐ The recipient of the value.

A good way to set priorities in your value stream mapping efforts is to focus on the value streams:

☐ With the highest volume.
☐ That concern your department.
☐ That you are most familiar with.

Chapter 3: Identify the Processes

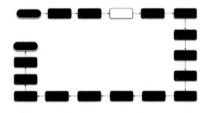

For the first two phases of the value stream mapping roadmap we asked you go to the end of the value stream to identify the value and the customer, the recipient of that value. You saw that those key elements of the value stream are not always completely straightforward to define, like the travel coffee mug we used as an example. These two initial phases of our roadmap gave you a good opportunity to think about the end point of the value stream under your scrutiny. By now you need to have a very clear picture of where the value is transferred to the customer. You know where this value stream ends, and you physically visited that place on multiple occasions to do your research.

We are now going to ask you to make sure that you understand where the value stream *begins* and develop the same sense of certainty you have with respect to the end point. Let's remember the value stream we are using as your example throughout the book: *the reprocessing of instrument sets for the OR.* Our recommendation, after have done a few of these projects, is to define the starting point of this particular value stream as the time when the OR suite changeover begins and the OR team starts re-loading the case cart. Some of you may not use case carts, and if not, focus on the time when the instrument set is no longer in use by the surgical team.

Based on how we have defined this value stream, it starts in the OR at the end of a case and it ends in the OR suite for the next case setup. This does not mean that we are looking at the same OR suite in both cases. The instrument set may travel from room to room, and hence the value stream may start in OR 1 and end in OR 12. Where the instrument set is eventually used is irrelevant.

Since you now have a very clear picture of the start and end point of the value stream you are analyzing, you are ready to take the next step, and the next step involves steps. You are now going to physically walk the path the instrument set follows from the beginning to the end of the value stream. Go ahead, put the book down and go for a stroll. The book will be waiting for you.

Welcome back! Let's now go over the trip you took. You must have seen the case cart getting loaded in the OR, the instruments being sprayed with enzymatic foam, the cart pushed to an elevator, the cart placed in queue at the decontamination side of the sterile processing department, linen unloaded from the cart, maybe trash unloaded also, instruments unloaded. At this time, the case cart and the instruments part ways and you followed the instrument set. We are sure that you can keep going with this list. The common thread across everything you describe when you follow the case cart and the instrument set is *work*. That work is being applied to the instrument set to advance it towards its point of completion, the end of the value stream. At that point, what is now a dirty set will become the value the customers are waiting for.

The work you just saw during your walk is exactly what you need to document. That work comes in many flavors: sometimes it is pushing, sometimes it is loading, sometimes it is washing, sometimes it is assembling, sometimes it is wrapping. You have now taken a dive to the next level of detail in a value stream. You went from the value stream level to the process level. This makes it very clear that *a value stream is made up of processes.*

A process is defined as a collection of like-work steps that advance the value in the direction of the customer. A process is work, performed by a person, a machine, or a combination of both. A process must have a clear starting point, a clear end point, and a definite series of tasks or work steps that take place sequentially between those two points. That was a lot of words to say *look for the work.*

One recommendation we always make is that the entire team takes the walk along the value stream and they all document the processes they see. For that, you may want to use a standard form so everybody works from the same format. That should simplify the discussion that will ensue. We will show you a format below and we will make it available to you at the Flow Publishing website.

As you walk the value stream from start to finish, look for the processes, give each one a unique short name and describe the work in just a few words. Another important aspect of understanding a process is that work does not always turn out in the way you expect. Sometimes, you do work and for one reason or another you have to do it over. We refer to this as *rework*. This is very common in the sterile processing value stream. For processes that do have rework, you need to find out how often the work has to be re-done. That will be the *rework percentage*.

Sometimes things are even worse than rework. There may be some cases where the work has gone so bad that the unit of value has to be thrown away. This is what is known as *scrap*. If you find a process that has scrap, you also need to determine the scrap percentage. In the value stream we are reviewing for our example, it would be very rare to find scrap, but not impossible. If the scrap rate is very low, we recommend you ignore it, as it will not impact the goals of the value stream analysis.

One more element that will be useful is to understand what resources are necessary to carry out the process work. The resources may be staff (OR tech, SPD tech, OR nurse) or machines (washer-disinfector, autoclave, Sterrad). There may be some other special services like compressed air that may be necessary. It is not necessary to document hand tools, as they are portable.

This is also a very good time to think about sustainability of results. This may sound a bit premature, but it is very critical. One of the keys to sustainability of results is to identify a *process owner*. The process owner is the staff member that has responsibility for the process' performance, the process documentation, and the staff training. Whenever you and your team come up with ideas to improve the process, the process owner must be involved to ensure he/she will carry out the necessary tasks to make the improvements stick. The process owner will also be expected to support further continuous improvement activities for the process.

When you put all the necessary data into one table it is going to look like the one shown on the next page.

We partially populated some sample processes for illustration purposes. Each row from the table above will (most likely) be documented on the value stream map. If you go back to the illustration of the initial value stream map, you will see two process boxes waiting to be labeled.

Well, it seems that your value stream map is going to have around a dozen processes. You will start drawing those process relationships in the next chapter.

Process ID	Description	Resources	Rework	Scrap	Owner
Reload Case Cart					
Break Cart Down					
Soak					
Machine Wash					
Cool Down					
Re-Assemble					
Wrap					
Load					
Autoclave					
Store					
Peel Pack					
Sterrad					

Chapter 3 Knowledge Check

What is the best way to identify the processes that will be included on your VSM?

- ☐ Brainstorm the processes with your team in a conference room.
- ☐ Research the processes from data available in your electronic medical records system.
- ☐ Walk the value stream with a pencil and paper in hand.

What is the best definition of a process?

- ☐ A collection of like-work steps that advance the value in the direction of the customer.
- ☐ A person or a machine doing work.
- ☐ A detailed work step on a procedure.

If work needs to be done over because of errors, this is something that you need to document on your value stream map. What is this type of work called?

- ☐ Scrap
- ☐ Rework
- ☐ The Waste of Overprocessing
- ☐ The Waste of Overproduction

Chapter 4: Draw the Process Relationships

Now we are ready to take the list of processes we created by surveying the value stream and develop a flowchart that  displays the flow of value across processes as the value progresses towards the customer at the end of the value stream.

We now need to introduce some VSM symbols and choose the ones that apply to the value stream at hand. You started with the initial VSM where all but two of the processes are missing, while the start and end points are displayed according to the agreed-upon convention.

You will notice that the illustrations in this book were done by hand, and this is the approach that we recommend when you first create your VSM. There are software tools that are available, that will help you document the value stream map more formally. The use of VSM software is not the first step.

The symbols you are most likely to use to draw value stream maps for the OR, and the hospital in general, are:

The Process Box

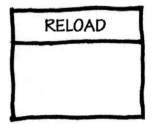

The Push Arrow

The Data Box

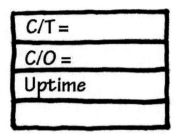

The Queue Symbol

The Connection Arrow

The Kaizen Burst

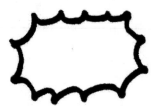

There will be other symbols but their utilization is very low compared to these.

Before you reach for the pens and the sticky notes, let's review the basic conventions. The canvas you will be using needs to look like this:

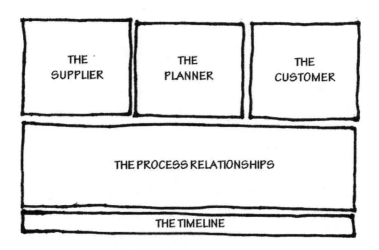

Notice that we have already located the customer in the figure above, and there is no supplier strictly speaking, so we use the upper left-hand corner of the chart for the starting point of the value stream map. Your goal in this phase of the roadmap is to populate the area labeled "THE PROCESS RELATIONSHIPS". This is where you will display the relationship of processes to deliver one unit of value. Do not look at the entire volume of work going through, focus on *just one unit of value*. If the value stream you are mapping describes patient flow from admission to pre-surg to the OR to PACU to discharge, follow only one patient. For the example we are looking into, we will follow just one instrument set.

You already went on a walk through the value stream and saw the processes with your own eyes. You documented those processes in a table, as required in Phase 3 of the Roadmap. You now have to take those processes, one at a time, and graphically display the relationship among them to complete one instrument set.

Feel free to either start from the beginning of the value stream and walk to the end, or to start at the end and walk upstream. In our experience with hospitals, the vast majority of value stream maps can be documented by starting at the beginning. The only case in which starting at the end of the value stream is more-or-less unavoidable is when a value stream has a definite end point but multiple start points. In that case, you will want to map from the end. This need is rare in hospitals.

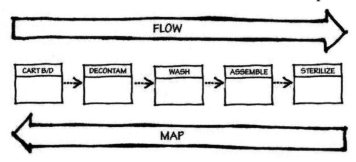

This is how we recommend you go about drawing the value stream map.

Preparation

- Have your supplies ready. Butcher paper, masking tape, a few color markers, four or five packs of color sticky-notes (3" X 3").

- Dress the wall with some butcher paper to prevent staining it with the markers.

Execution

- Ask for a volunteer to write the process names on the sticky notes. Hand him/her all the markers and notes. Let's refer to this volunteer as *the scribe*.

- Draw the start and end points of the value stream.

- Write all relevant data near the start and end points like the customer, the end volume, and the value stream name.

- Ask the entire team to review with you all the processes they saw when you went together for a walk.

- Ask the team to tell you the first process they saw on the value stream. Ask the team to give that process a short name, preferably one word. Ask the scribe to write the process name on the sticky note and hand it to you.

- Attach that first process to the left-most position of process area.

- Ask the team to tell you the second process they saw during their walk. Again, ask the team to give that process a pithy name and ask the scribe to jot it down on a sticky note of the same color used before. Stick with that same color for all processes.

- Repeat until all processes are on the wall.

- As you work with the team, go back to the processes already documented and review them to make sure there is consensus.

- Go over the entire set of processes and draw arrows depicting the relationship of those processes to one-another as defined by the flow of value across the value stream.

After completing this phase, the value stream map is likely to look like the illustration on the next page.

At this stage you know how the processes you saw with your own eyes relate to one another to yield one unit of value at the end of the value stream. In this example, the unit of value is an instrument set back in the OR suite and ready for use.

The next question you need to answer is "How long does it take to do the work at each process?" This needs to be answered while keeping in mind that you are following only one unit of value.

Value Stream Map: Draw the Process Relationships.

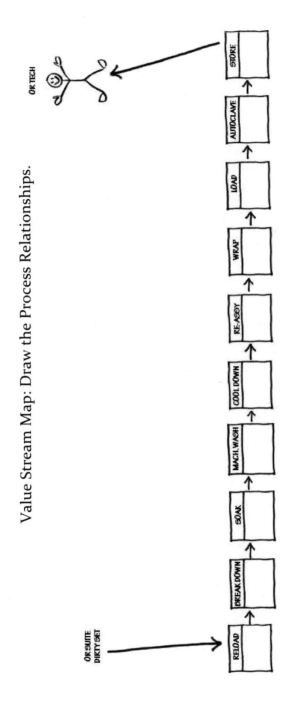

Chapter 4 Knowledge Check

You will sometimes document a value stream by starting at the end and working your way upstream. Why?

☐ That's the way that Toyota does it.
☐ Walking backwards give the team a fresh perspective on the process.
☐ You don't always know where the beginning of a value stream is, or there may be multiple start points.

True or False: When you draw your value stream map, it is recommended to do it using computer software from the start. That will save a lot of time later on, and it also looks much cleaner.

☐ True
☐ False

When you draw a value stream map, you follow a prescribed format. Why?

☐ By following the same format, we know where to look for the various elements of the VSM, even on ones we haven't seen before.
☐ The eye naturally reads from left to right, at least in the West.
☐ The format has been taught and adapted as a standard around the world.
☐ All of the above reasons.

Chapter 5: Establish Process Times

One of the most important measurements that you need to gather, and one that is often not available from existing data, is the *time needed to complete each process*. In a manufacturing environment time studies are common and expected, and establishing time standards for work is nothing new. In people-centric healthcare, however, the work is inherently more variable and less repetitive. People are not machines, and the time required to examine, care for and treat human beings, even for exactly the same procedure, will fall into a much wider range than other types of work.

That said, however, we need to acknowledge that even healthcare work time falls within *some* boundaries. Otherwise it would be extremely difficult to schedule appointments, maintain surgical times or manage hospital staff. Most work, in fact, includes some expectation of what constitutes a *reasonable* time, and in the majority of cases this time can actually be achieved. It is known with a fair degree of accuracy how long certain procedures normally take, for example. Non-clinical work can be even more accurately timed. The number of minutes to complete a form, to enter data into an electronic medical record system, or turn over a patient room, should all fall within a fairly narrow range of times.

Of course you can always think of exceptions to the rule, on either extreme, but what you are interested in for purposes of capturing process times on a value stream map are *reasonable average times* for the processes documented. We need to repeat again and again that the VSM process is like flying at 30,000 feet and assessing the contours of the land below. You are not concerned with the "correct" time for a process, as long as you are confident that the times captured are reasonable. In fact there is no "right" time.

If you have not done a time study for the value stream in question, and chances are that you have not, you have two options regarding work time: making an educated guess and actually timing staff members doing the work. There are pros and cons to both approaches. An educated guess is certainly easier than actually timing the work, but it is still a guess that could be way off. Timing staff doing the work is more accurate, but may also be biased by the skill of the individuals being studied, or by people working faster or slower because they know they are being timed.

In our experience, the work pace you will see by observing and timing work tends to be faster if staff members know that they are being timed. There is a natural tendency to think that you are being evaluated, and people focus on their work more if they are being watched. If you suspect that this is the case, you might want to round up your times a bit to account for this phenomenon.

On the other hand, in certain work environments people may tend to slow down when they think they are being timed. This will most often happen when people believe that management is trying to get them to work faster, and to reset expectations for the work pace.

A good timing technique that is especially easy to do these days is to record the work on a video camera. You should not record the work in secret, of course, but a camera running in the corner of the room is less intimidating than a person with a stop watch, and you will get more reasonable times using this technique. Another advantage of video is that you can view the work and document the times without worrying about missing something. You can watch the video as many times as necessary to understand and document the work correctly.

Most value stream maps will include many individual processes, so be prudent about what needs to be timed closely and what can be estimated. Very short processes will have less impact on the total time, for example. The processes that should be looked at more closely are the problem children, the processes that you know from experience are a source of delay and pain. Apply the 80/20 rule: probably only 20% of the total processes need a closer look, and probably 80% of the work time is those 20% of the processes.

There is one other time study you will need to complete, which we will discuss in more detail in an upcoming chapter. This one is a unique feature of value stream mapping, and it may make sense to document this time now if possible. In most flow-charting methods other than VSM, you draw a process box and an arrow showing the flow of work. Any queue time or waiting time *between* processes is simply ignored. Not so with value stream mapping. You will need to come up with a reasonable average wait time *between processes,* an estimate of the average time that the value is waiting before being worked on by the subsequent process. Every delay between processes on your current state VSM will need an estimate for queue time.

A common response to this request is, "We can't estimate wait time, since it varies so much." Yes, we understand that the queue time can be zero at times, and we also understand that it sometimes can be many hours or days. What you are looking for is a *reasonable average queue time,* based on your team's experience. Don't waste time on fruitless debate. You probably won't be able to observe the queue time easily, so use an estimate. You can fine-tune this data further down the road if necessary.

The unit of time that makes the most sense for hospital work and queue time is *minutes*, as opposed to hours or seconds. Trying to time work that is so inherently variable in increments of seconds is an exercise in irrelevance, and whole hours of time is too high level. Stick to minutes of time, and round up any fractions of a minute you may record.

In this chapter we discussed the need to record process time for both work that is done and the queue time between processes. Focus on the most important or painful processes for detailed analysis, and rely on your team's judgment for many of the others. Most of all, don't be afraid of documenting the "wrong" time at this stage of your Lean evolution. There will be opportunities to fine-tune your number when we talk about *Standard Work Definitions* in a future chapter.

Chapter 5 Knowledge Check

How does the 80/20 rule apply to documenting times for your value stream mapping project?

- ☐ Time 80% of the processes, and estimate the remaining 20%.
- ☐ 80% of the total time is represented by only 20% of the processes. Focus on these to start.
- ☐ 80% of the hospital revenue is generated by only 20% of the patients.

When staff members are timed they tend to:

- ☐ Speed up because they think they are being evaluated.
- ☐ Slow down because they think management is trying to get them to work faster.
- ☐ Speed up or slow down depending on the hospital culture.

The best times to use in your value stream map are:

- ☐ The work time for the fastest staff member.
- ☐ A reasonable average time for a trained person in the process.
- ☐ An estimate by management of what the work time *should* be.

Chapter 6: Gather Process Ancillary Data

In the previous chapter we discussed the capturing of process times for each process. In this chapter we will examine the other types  of information you will want to know about a process, and which you can document on your value stream map. To help you in this analysis we'll refer to the *data box* feature included in the iGrafx VSM software tool, as shown below.

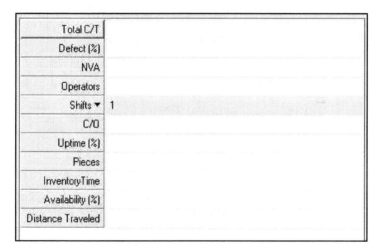

These categories shown here are the default data metrics that are included with this software tool, although it is also possible to create and add user-defined metrics. As we will see, many of these items are more pertinent to a manufacturing environment, and we will skip over them quickly. We will also be adding a few user-defined metrics that will be useful. Shown below is the updated data box, with the new metrics added, with unneeded metrics removed, and with more hospital-friendly terms substituted.

Work Time	
Defect Percent (%)	
NVA	
Staff	
Shifts ▼	1
Changeover Time	
Delay	
Availability (%)	
Distance Traveled	
Process Maturity Level	
Standard Work Definition	

It's important to know that not all of these measurements are necessary to capture, and not all of them are applicable to every process. Only two of the metrics, work time and delay, have an impact on the timeline that we will create at the bottom of the VSM. The other metrics will be used to help identify opportunities for improvement, where the current measurement clearly indicates a need. For example, if we notice that the *distance traveled* for a particular process is high, that would be an indicator to identify ways to reduce the amount of travel, since motion is classified as one of the Lean wastes.

Here's what the process box looks like on your value stream map. You place it directly below the process box, and enter whatever metrics you are able to gather for that process. A sticky note works just fine.

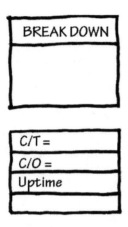

Following is a description of each of the data fields listed.

Work Time

This data element was described in the previous chapter. As stated, this time will include both value-added work and non-value-added work for the process being documented. As you refine your waste-elimination efforts in the future you will want to take a close look at wasted activity, such as unnecessary walking, but for purposes of value stream mapping you will want to just capture the total time required to complete the process, both value-adding and non-value-adding. The abbreviation C/T means Cycle Time, another common term for work time.

Defect %

If the work that is done in this process is sometimes done wrong, and requires some rework, that would be a good thing to know as a part of the VSM process and a clear opportunity for improvement. In Chapter 10 we will be discussing the stage of brainstorming improvements, and any process that has a significant level of errors or defects will be a prime candidate to work on. If hard data is available for the percent of defects, then use that number. Otherwise enter an educated guess. You don't need to be concerned if you're a percentage or two off in your estimate.

NVA

This term should by now be familiar to you: Non-Value-Adding. We already said that the work time data element includes both VA and NVA time. This additional data element can be used if the amount of NVA time is known. Otherwise leave it blank. During the brainstorming improvements phase we will want to focus on the processes that have a high percentage of NVA time, so that this data element can be very useful to know.

Staff

The data element *staff* refers to the number of staff members that work in this process, across all shifts.

This again can be a very useful data point when we discuss process improvements. Processes that involve a larger number of staff members will merit more intense scrutiny than processes that only involve a few people, all other factors being equal.

Shifts

This is an easy one: how many shifts does this process work during the 24-hour cycle? Normally this data element is for reference only, but occasionally it will make sense to adjust shift schedules to achieve a smoother flow across processes, and knowing this information will come in handy.

Changeover Time

If there is some preparation work required between patients or products, we call this work *changeover* or *turnover* time. Since we are preparing for the next patient and not actually treating a patient during the changeover time, this work is classified as non-value-adding. Processes that have long changeover times are a ripe target for the methods of *quick changeover,* documented in our book *Quick Changeover in the OR.* OR suite changeover between patients is a prime example of this type of work, as is patient room changeover.

Delay

Delay is a very important piece of information, described in more detail in a separate chapter,

Identify Process Delays. Suffice it to say here that we expect to see some delay between *every* process, unless the work always flows directly from one process to another.

Availability

There may be some conditions under which a process is not available, usually expressed as a percentage of the total work time. For example, we may discover that 10% of the time a washer-disinfector is non-functioning, or that the cart tunnel washer is down 25% of the time. Document that percentage here.

Distance Traveled

There are two types of Lean waste related to distance: motion and transportation. The waste of motion refers to movement on the part of staff that does not add value to the patient. When we have to walk from one place to another, looking for the extra-large back table, chances are high that you are not actually adding value. Of course you are still on the payroll, and of course the walking is necessary to get from one place to another, but while you are walking you are probably not caring for a patient or entering information into your electronic medical record system. Motion also applies to the movement that may take place in a single area, that again does not represent value-adding-work. A spaghetti diagram, a drawing of all of the motion that takes place to complete a job, can vividly show the amount of motion that is sometimes required to get the job done.

The second type of waste that involves distance is that of transportation. Transportation refers not to the movement that you do as a staff member, but rather to the movement of patients or value in general. Moving the patient from the OR to PACU, for example, is classified as transportation. Medications that are delivered from the pharmacy to a nursing floor is another example of transportation. The waste of transportation is similar to that of motion, in that we are probably not adding value to the care of the patient while she is being moved. If we didn't need to move the patient at all, she would probably be just as happy or happier.

A significant amount of motion or transportation can be a great opportunity for improvement, and hence it is useful to document this information on your value stream map. Motion can be measured with a pedometer, and you may be surprised at the distance travelled during a normal working day. Transportation can be measured by pacing off the distance, or more accurately by using a *measuring wheel*.

The distance moved between processes can be documented at the bottom of the Value Stream map, in a format similar to that used to document process times.

Process Maturity Level

Establishing the process maturity level for a process is an extremely useful data element, since a process with low maturity will be difficult to manage and sustain. Let's first define the five levels of process maturity, and then discuss how we will use this information.

Level 1 (the lowest level): Your process has a name and a general definition of the work that is done in that process. You may even have a flow-chart of the work being done in the process, but detailed work instructions do not exist.

Level 2. The process has been documented to the work step level. Every work step has been written down, the necessary quality checks have been defined, and process times have been taken for each work step.

Level 3. Individuals who work in this process have been trained in standard work, documented previously in Level 2. It does little good to document a process if staff members are not actually following it, and Level 3 ensures that the defined *one best way* is being followed. Note that simply sharing the process information is not enough. Staff members need to demonstrate their ability to do standard work, and supervisors and managers need to ensure that adherence is sustained over time.

Level 4. We don't expect any process to be perfect, and Level 4 is *engagement,* the involvement of all staff members who work in the process in making it better. Implicit in this effort is the existence of measurements, so that we know where we stand at any point in time. A high level of employee involvement is one of the key characteristics of a mature Lean organization.

Level 5, Sustaining Improvements. You can say that you are at Level 5 maturity in a process if you have been able to demonstrate a track record of continuous improvement for at least 12 months, based on the metrics previously defined.

What importance does the Process Maturity Scale have on your value stream mapping efforts? If the process in question is not at Level 3 or better, then the initial process improvement needs to be focused on process documentation and stabilization. If staff members are not following standard work today, how can you expect them to follow any other process improvements that may be introduced? If we are not at Level 3, then getting there becomes your highest priority for process improvement.

Standard Work Definition

This metric refers to the existence or non-existence of detailed work instructions for the process in question, and is also related to the process maturity scale discussed above as Level 2. Developing standard work definitions is no minor detail, but like they say about the cost of education, consider the alternative. If many of your key processes are at less than Level 3 on the process maturity scale, then you know where much of your initial process improvement effort will be.

As we showed you above, add your process metrics to the *data box* below the process box. The minimum data we expect to see in the data box is the process time, which is non-optional. From here we can proceed to the documentation of the time between processes, the *process queue time*.

On the next page we added the data boxes to each process with the minimum data of process times.

Value Stream Map: Process Boxes and Data Boxes.

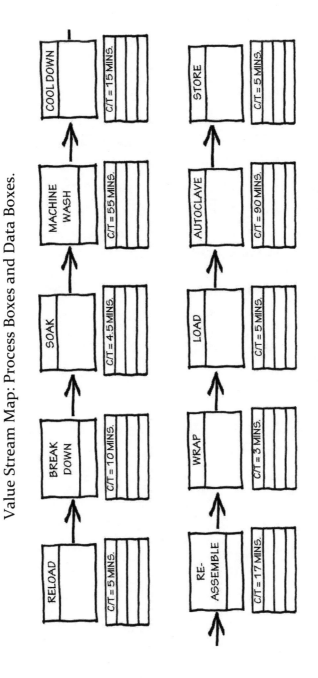

Chapter 6 Knowledge Check

What is the minimum level of process maturity you should achieve before you engage in other improvements in the process?

- ☐ Level 1: the process has a name and an owner.
- ☐ Level 2: the process is documented to the work instruction level.
- ☐ Level 3: the staff working in the process are trained and certified.
- ☐ Level 4: the process is managed with data and has a high level of staff engagement.

True or False: Processes with a high defect percent should be the highest priority for process improvement efforts.

- ☐ True
- ☐ False

A useful tool for assessing the amount of movement or distance traveled is called the:

- ☐ Linguini Diagram
- ☐ Throw It Against the Wall Chart
- ☐ Spaghetti Diagram
- ☐ The Roadmap

Chapter 7: Identify Process Delays

One of the unique differences between value stream mapping and other flow-charting techniques, including process mapping, is the requirement to document wait time or queue time between process steps. In a typical flow chart wait time between processes is simply ignored; only the work itself is captured. You draw a series of boxes and arrows, and the assumption is that the work simply flows from one step to the next. The truth of the matter, however, is usually very different, and the documenting of process delays make value stream mapping an especially valuable tool.

A careful analysis of any value stream, and especially one that has not been "leaned out" or improved, will reveal a high percentage of process delay as compared to the total elapsed time. It is not unusual to observe that over 90% of the elapsed time represents process delay or wait time, and only 10% or less is work time or value adding time. If this claim sounds too bad to be true, just take a stop watch, a pencil and a pad of paper to the OR, to the ED, or any other major value stream in a hospital, staple yourself to an incoming patient (metaphorically) and record the times when the patient is being attended to versus the time when the patient is waiting. You will become quickly convinced that the 90% figure is no exaggeration. Why do you think they call it the *Waiting Room*?

There is some good news. Because process delays represent a high percentage of the total time, and since by definition no value adding work is being done during that time, great improvements in the patient experience can be achieved without having to change the work processes themselves at all. That's not to say that work processes should not be improved, of course, but the process delays are the *low hanging fruit* improvements that can be easier to achieve. The patients also notice and appreciate less delay, as you can easily imagine.

Here are the instructions on how to document the processes delays between processes on a value stream map. Presumably at this stage you have captured all of the processes in the value stream that you are documenting, often in the form of sticky notes on a wall. You know the processes and you know how they are related in time. The question that the team will now answer for every process, starting with the first one, is "When the work is completed in the first process (reload case cart), does the subsequent process (case cart breakdown) always start immediately?" If the answer is yes, there *is* no process delay between these two processes. If the answer is no, then the team will need to estimate an average delay time between the end of the first process and the start of the next process. Someone on the team is certain to point out that this delay time is not consistent. Sometimes it could be zero and sometimes it could be two days, for example. Don't get hung up on a debate as to the "correct" delay time, unless you have some hard data to refer to, which is unlikely. Just reach a consensus with the team on a reasonable and average delay time, document it on your value stream map, and move on. Remind the team that you are flying at 30,000 feet, and that at this stage in your Lean journey you are just trying to get a feel for the lay of the land.

Here's an important point, sometimes overlooked. Unless two processes are directly connected, so that the patient or value (instrument set) always flows from one to the other, there will *always* be some delay between processes that will need to be documented. After all, unless the receiving process is always available, and not working on anything else, then you can expect some delay whenever there is a hand-off from person to person or department to department. To be brutally honest, you should expect to see a delay documented between *just about every process.*

Is there any process delay that is too small to bother with? Unless the process delay is measured in mere seconds, write it down. A one-minute delay is not going to attract a lot of improvement effort compared to a one-day delay, but let's document it. We'll get to it eventually.

Here's an example of how this stage in your value stream analysis might be conducted. Let's start with a simple and common pair of processes: the reload of a case cart and the breaking down of the cart in the decontamination side of the sterile processing department. Before adding any process delays your Value Stream Map would look something like this:

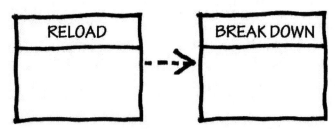

The broken arrow connecting the two processes is a *push* arrow, signifying that the reload work is pushed to the next process without needing any signal or permission. The case cart gets moved to the decontamination area for breakdown, regardless of the workload that may already be waiting for processing. We'll talk about alternatives to push in the chapter on brainstorming improvements.

The sequence of questions for the value stream mapping team will be as follows:

1. When the case cart arrives at breakdown, the second process, is it always worked on immediately? The answer is usually no, because

the staff in breakdown is probably already busy working on another case cart. The new work will go into a queue, and get processed in first-in first-out order. *Could* the instrument set get processed right away? Sure, but there's no guarantee of that happening.

2. Since you have established that a process delay exists between these two processes, how much of a delay can you expect? The answer from the team is usually "that depends". It could be very little delay, or the wait could be up to two hours, which would be rare.

Reach a consensus among the team regarding a reasonable average time. In this example the team agrees that a one hour process delay would be a reasonable average time.

You add the process delay to your Value Stream Map, as shown below:

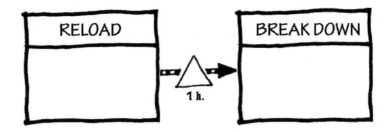

Note that the symbol we use for process delay is a triangle, pointing up. The delay time can be written inside the triangle or immediately below it.

In the value stream map on the next page we added the delay times identified by the VSM team, that were either estimated or measured.

Some of you may be uncomfortable with the idea of "guesstimating" the average process delay, and would prefer to have better actual data. In most cases having more data on process delays is not going to help your improvement process, but if there are cases of significant delay in your value stream that are major pain points, you will want to capture actual times. For example, waiting to be seen in the Emergency Room is a major concern, and most hospitals *do* track this delay within their computer system. If you don't have an automated way of collecting this time, you will need to conduct a study, create a log book, and manually collect this data over a reasonable period of time. Once you have enough data points, you can calculate an average time based on better numbers. You plan to complete a value stream analysis in a few days, so in most cases let's take an educated guess at the process delay, and if necessary gather more detailed information at a later time.

In the next chapter we'll take the value stream analysis to the next step, the calculation of some performance metrics that you will want to track. Don't worry, it's just simple arithmetic.

Value Stream Map: Process Boxes, Data Boxes and Queue Time.

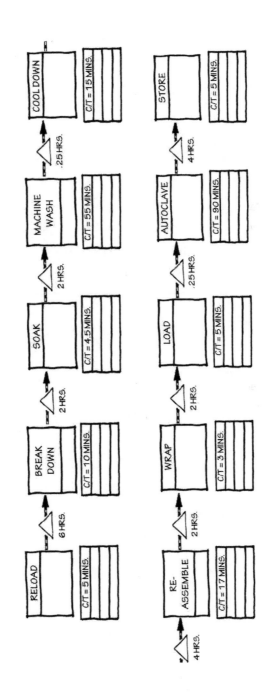

Chapter 7 Knowledge Check

The symbol used to designate wait or queue time between processes is the:

☐ Triangle pointing down.
☐ Triangle pointing up.
☐ The castle wall.
☐ The data box.

True or False: Whenever work is passed from one department to another, you expect to see some waiting taking place.

☐ True
☐ False

Since waiting time between processes can vary greatly, you should:

☐ Use the worst case time, based on your experience.
☐ Use an average time, based on your experience.
☐ Conduct a detailed time study of the actual queue times, in order to develop an accurate measurement.

Chapter 8: Calculate Performance Metrics

You now have a completed *current state value stream map,* including process delays and a completed data box. Congratulations,  but there is one more step that you need to complete before you get to the exciting phase of identifying opportunities for improvement and creating the *future state value stream map.* If you are to have an idea of the potential improvement in this value stream, and be able to justify the effort and expense that will be needed to improve it, you need to have some data. You will use the current state value stream map to set the baseline measurements, and once you have created the future state you'll have some numbers to compare to. Follow along as we calculate performance metrics on the current state value stream map.

At the bottom of the VSM, below the process boxes and data boxes going from left to right, you will first draw the timeline, also called the *castle wall.* Start with the first process by drawing a horizontal line about the same width as the process box above, and write the total process time above the line. An example of this is shown below.

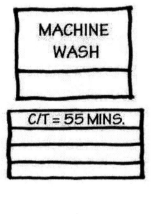

If there is a delay between this process and the next one, as indicated by the triangle symbol, then draw a step up and a horizontal line under the triangle symbol, and write the total delay time above this line. The example below shows this next step.

Continue on until you have captured all of the process times and the delay times at the bottom of the VSM. The drawing should now look like a castle wall, albeit an uneven one.

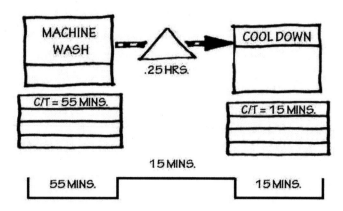

Finally add up all of the process times and all of the delay times and write them down on the lower right side of the VSM. You will also want to calculate the percentage of process time versus the total time. Don't be surprised if the process time is only a small percentage of the total time including delays. It would not be unusual to see a 9 to 1 ratio of total time to the actual work time.

As an optional step you can now create a distance line underneath the castle wall to display and sum the total distance traveled, as documented in the data boxes above. Total the distanced traveled on the right side of the VSM, as you did with the process times.

What other results can you calculate from the current state value stream map? Following below is a listing of possibilities based on the data documented in the data boxes under each process. The expectation for each of these performance metrics is that you will be making improvements to reach the future state, and you need to compare these potential improvements with where you are today. As much as possible you would like to express your gains in the common denominator of cold hard cash. While this isn't always possible or easy (improvements in staff satisfaction, for example), converting improvements to dollars allows us to compare various opportunities directly.

Work Time	
Defect Percent [%]	
NVA	
Staff	
Shifts ▾	1
Changeover Time	
Delay	
Availability [%]	
Distance Traveled	
Process Maturity Level	
Standard Work Definition	

Defect Percent. If you have processes that allow defects and errors, these processes immediately become a high priority for improvement in your future state VSM. A percentage is less meaningful than the actual number of incidents, or the cost related to these defects. For example, if 5% of your case carts arriving in the OR have some kind of issue that needs to be addressed, and your hospital does 10,000 procedures per year, that translates to 500 case carts that need to be reworked. Assign a dollar value, including the potential impact of delays, to each incident, and you will have an estimate of the dollar impact of this metric.

Staff. If you eliminate waste from a process, it is logical to expect that you would need fewer people in that process as well. In a hospital environment you would like to reinvest that freed-up time back into patient care, and reduce workplace stress, rather than considering process improvements as an opportunity to reduce headcount. More than that, before embarking on a Lean initiative hospital management needs to understand and pledge not to reduce staff due to process improvements. *Associating process improvements and layoffs will be the kiss of death for future improvement initiatives.*

Turnover/Changeover Time. There may be some processes with significant changeover time, and these will be an opportunity for improvement using the quick changeover method. In your summary table show the total changeover hours per year by multiplying the average changeover time for a process by the number of cases per year. For example, if it currently takes 35 minutes to change an OR suite, and your hospital does 10,000 procedures per year, the hospital is spending 5,833 hours a year on OR suite changeover. This type of data is easy to quantify, by assigning a dollar value to each OR suite hour.

Average Process Maturity Level. If you have measured the process maturity level of each process, as discussed before, then an average process maturity level would be an excellent thing to know for your entire value stream. Remember that your goal is to get to Level 3 at least, so anything less than that is a clear indicator of the actions that need to take place in getting to the future state. For example, if your current average process maturity level is 2.2, that indicates that you have some processes that are not documented to the work instruction level, and that you don't have a training and certification process in place. Your master plan will need to address these deficiencies as a high priority.

Document these additional metrics in a table on the right side of your VSM document. You'll be referring to it often as you develop your future state VSM, with the objective of making significant improvements.

You're now ready for the fun part, although the work up to now has not been particularly painful, right? You're now ready to launch your process improvement efforts, by first identifying waste in the value stream clearly, and then by coming up with Lean-based improvements.

Value Stream Map: Process Boxes, Data Boxes, Queue and Timeline.

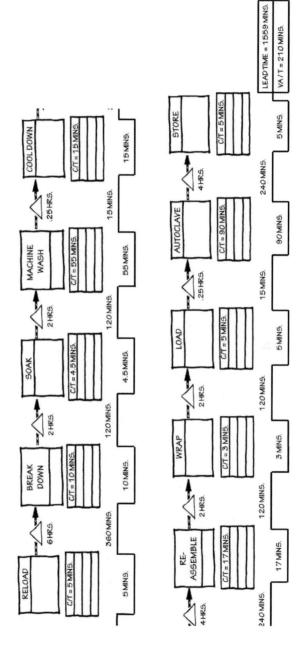

Chapter 8 Knowledge Check

The difference between the total elapsed time in a value stream as compared to the work time could be as much as:

☐   2 to 1
☐   5 to 1
☐   9 to 1
☐   20 to 1

It is critical to avoid associating process improvement efforts with any headcount reductions. Why?

☐ Participation in continuous improvements will drop to zero if staff perceived that it leads to layoffs.
☐ The hospital needs to avoid lawsuits that could be triggered by headcount reductions.
☐ This should be a non-issue since it is rare that Lean improvements improve productivity.

The drawing at the bottom of the page that you use to summarize work time and queue time is commonly called the:

☐ The Berlin Wall
☐ The Castle Wall
☐ The Time Summary
☐ The Process Box

Chapter 9: Identify Sources of Waste

At this stage in your journey you have in front of you an accurate current state value stream map, with queue times, timeline and  performance metrics documented. You are not discouraged by the fact that you have not made any actual improvements yet, and that at least so far your work appears to have been *waste*. Don't worry, you will get there, but before you start coming up with improvements you need to know what the problems are. That's the subject of this chapter. Once you've identified the problems you will then create solutions, the subject of Chapter 10.

Our value stream analysis leads directly to an analysis of waste in the value stream, work that adds cost and time but doesn't add value to the customer. We have organized the topic of waste into nine categories, based on the famous *seven wastes* of the Toyota Production System adapted for an OR environment. Your value stream mapping team needs to be familiar with these sources of waste, in order to be able to see them clearly. Following is a short description of each of the nine categories.

Overproduction. This form of waste takes place when you produce more than what is needed right now by the customer. Examples of this waste in the Perioperative Services department are:

1. Reassembling instrument sets in large batches while the autoclave sits idle. The symptom is "We do not have enough instrument sets."

2. Spiking IV bags in Pre-Surgery for the whole day, while patients wait. The symptom is "Our on-time starts are very low."

Here's the Lean rule: any production in excess of your short-term needs can be considered waste. Even if you have a very good reason why you overproduce, this does not change the fact that excessive production is waste. The process needs to be improved to allow the efficient production of smaller quantities, in line with actual needs.

Transportation. You see this form of waste when the patient or the value (instrument set) is moved *without* adding value. Examples of this form of waste are:

1. Blood specimens collected at the oncology unit go on a hospital tour before reaching the lab.

2. IV and DVT pumps go from the patient room to sterile processing and back via utility rooms, for a few seconds of cleaning.

As was the case with over-production, you can't just say "stop doing that" to eliminate this waste. It requires you to ask *why* in a more forceful way, and to come up with practical alternatives. Remember that the waste exists for a reason, typically related to bad processes.

Motion. This form of waste refers to staff members moving without adding value. This becomes evident in the amount of walking staff members do during their day, looking or "hunting" for something. Why is it that you cannot provide clinicians with the tools and supplies they need to take care of patients? Some examples of motion waste are:

1. Searching for a patient lift, a positioning device, an IV pump or any piece of equipment. The level of frustration staff members feel when they cannot find what they need is enormous. Delay of care can also be dangerous for the patient.

2. Searching for paperwork. If your hospital still requires hand-written paperwork for surgical patients, you may find yourself scrambling for that document while the patient is on the table.

This is one of the easiest forms of waste to solve. The application of 7S methods and the abolishment of the *par level* system for supplies management will get you most of the way there.

Waiting. This is idle time created when supplies, information, people, and equipment are not ready. If you find yourself waiting on any kind of resource, you need to start asking why, and be ready to take action once you get the answer. Just one rule: blaming somebody else is not allowed. Here are some practical examples you can verify for yourself:

1. Take a stroll through the waiting rooms. How many patients do you see waiting?

2. Go to Pre-Surgery. How many patients are ready, but their OR is not?

3. Go to PACU. How many patients are recovered, but there is no room for them to be moved to?

Over-Processing. This is the waste of overdoing. It is so easy to believe you are doing the right thing by overdoing. Think about the times you do this at home: "If three screws will do, five must be better." Here are some more examples from the OR:

1. In one perioperative services department, staff was checking case carts four times, due to the unspoken distrust of the prior processes.

2. The par level method, where supplies are counted or eye-balled daily. See *Supplies Management in the OR* for our critique of this method and an excellent alternative.

Excess Inventory. When you see more supplies, equipment or paperwork than the customer needs right now, you have excess inventory. The OR is the champion of excess inventory in the hospital. The OR wants to have enough inventory in case the worst happens, and then double that in case the Martians attack. Excess inventory gives staff a false sense of security. When you need something, you then have to wade through piles of stuff to get to what you need. Are you seeing the waste yet? To that, add the increased risk of expired items due to the piles you have to go through. Pick a couple of well-stocked shelves and see if you find any expired supplies.

The main culprit is the incredible anachronistic par level system that many ORs use for supplies management, as we mentioned in the previous waste. It is mind boggling that hospitals still use such an inefficient method to deliver supplies to clinicians. Start by abolishing par. The result of implementing Lean supplies management will be a substantial reduction in inventory dollars coupled with the elimination of shortages. Here's what if often seen in the OR:

1. Topping off of supplies instead of observing the par levels previously established.

2. Eye-balling supplies instead of counting, since counting everything every day is virtually impossible.

3. Overstocking for weekends due to a disconnect between the supplies delivery schedule and OR needs.

Defects. Defects represent work that contains errors, requires rework, has mistakes or lacks something necessary. Nothing proclaims a broken process quite like defective work. The temptation is to start with the old search for accountability, and looking for someone to blame. Instead, try looking at the broken process and asking why, or use simple assessment tools like a fishbone diagram. Engage other staff members in finding solutions. The results will amaze you.

A typical OR example is that of an incomplete instrument set. Your choices are: "Accountability!" or, after you solve the immediate need ask: "Why was the set incomplete?"

1. Could it be that it was sent to SPD from the OR incomplete?

2. Could it be that you need to develop work instructions for each instrument set?

3. Could it be that the instrument was sent to sharpening?

Ineffective Use of Computers. This form of waste refers to time spent at the computer, but not using the available software efficiently. No one questions the fact that the use of computers is a must in a modern hospital. However, when their use detracts from patient care, you must stop and ask why.

Take another stroll and go to pre-surgery. Stand in the department and count the number of clinicians in patient rooms versus the number in front of a computer screen. What is the ratio? What should that ratio be?

Human Potential. The waste of human potential is not taking advantage of people's natural desire to be a part of something good. This is considered the biggest of the wastes, and by engaging staff you will identify and reduce or eliminate all the other forms of waste. This is not about the touchy-feely stuff like "Our staff is our most valuable asset" or "we practice respect for our people".

Show respect for staff by engaging them in working on solutions to the problems that afflict their processes. Check the results. You will be amazed.

Once these nine categories of waste have been understood and discussed by your value stream mapping team, review your current state VSM from the perspective of each of the wastes, one by one. Start with a critical waste, the waste of defects. As you know, defects in a hospital environment can be life-threatening, and if you have processes that you know are not error-proofed that is a good place to start. With your entire team in attendance, simple go process by process with your quality goggles on, and flag the VSM processes that need attention from a quality perspective. You don't need to come up with solutions yet, just flag the process.

Another low-hanging fruit opportunity is the waste of waiting. With your team look at the queue time between processes, the triangle symbol, and flag the instances where there is a clear need for improvement. Again, you don't need to have answers and solutions yet.

A third big opportunity spans a number of different waste categories, related to a low level of process maturity discussed above. If the process has no owner, is not well documented and the people working in the process are not well trained, you can expect a number of different wastes to emerge.

Team members with intimate knowledge of the details of the VSM processes can be very helpful in pointing out waste that is not easily seen on the VSM. For example, we have made it no secret that we consider the par level method highly dysfunctional, but your VSM team members may be able to point out other specific practices that need improvement. If supplies shortages are excessive, i.e. greater than zero, then that will be a target for improvement.

What you end up with at this phase of your VSM project is a current state value stream map with the areas of waste identified. Use a different colored sticky-note to identify these areas of opportunity. We're now ready for the most exciting part of this journey, the creation of solutions. About time, right?

Chapter 9 Knowledge Check

Why is the waste of human potential considered the biggest of all the nine wastes?

- ☐ Staff members are naturally inefficient, and a larger percentage of their work day is wasted.
- ☐ All people have ideas, but few organizations take advantage of employee creativity and enthusiasm.
- ☐ Staff members could easily work harder and faster, given proper supervision.

True or False: Transporting the case cart from the elevator to the OR suite cannot be considered waste because we have to do it.

- ☐ True
- ☐ False

True or False: A large inventory of supplies in the OR inner core is not waste because we will use the supplies eventually. It is only waste if we throw them away.

- ☐ True
- ☐ False

Chapter 10: Brainstorm Solutions

Don't get the impression that *brainstorming solutions* just means trying to be smart and come up with common sense 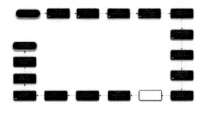 solutions to improving your value stream. You want to base your changes and suggestions on *Lean Thinking*, applying the best practices that have been developed over the years for eliminating waste from the value stream. Common sense is fine, of course, but if you have not been trained in Lean methods you probably are not yet aware of the ways in which common problems have already been solved in other hospitals and even in other industries. A part of your value stream mapping initiative therefore will include some formal training, in the nine wastes, in the concepts of push and pull, in the importance of standard work, and in the benefits of creating a visual workflow. It is also helpful to have an experienced mentor on your value stream mapping team, who will help to guide the discussion in the direction of Lean Thinking while still allowing the team to exercise independent decision-making. This mentor could be an internal resource, or an outside consultant with significant perioperative Lean experience.

There is, however, a creative aspect to problem solving that goes beyond copying what has been done elsewhere. If we could simply apply a prepackaged solution in every case, then every hospital would be world-class, so there is more to it than that. Achieving buy-in for your proposed solutions is also greatly enhanced if the ideas come from the team, with some skillful guidance from the Lean leaders. As Lao Tzu said over 2,500 years ago, "In the perfect society, the people say we did it ourselves."

As we have said above, quality of care considerations are foremost in our minds, so it makes sense to start with improvements directed towards eliminating errors. There is a Lean expression that describes this: poka-yoke or error-proofing. Error-proofing does not mean error reduction; it means the *elimination* of the possibility of error. In case you think that is impossible, you should know that there are many processes that are very close to being error-free. For example, airplane take-offs and landings have achieved a very high quality level. If not, given the number of takeoffs and landings that happen every day, we'd be reading about accidents all the time in the newspaper. You may have heard of the term six-sigma, a well-known approach to quality improvement. At the level of six sigma quality, you would expect 3.4 defects per million opportunities. At this level of quality the process is essentially defect-free.

Apply what you have learned about the process maturity model, which is typically your first step in improving process quality if the process is not well documented and staff members are not well trained. Relevant performance metrics, if not currently being tracked for the process, are another improvement that will be necessary to keep a process on the road to continuous improvement.

You will be using a special symbol to document an improvement idea on your value stream map, the kaizen burst. Kaizen is a Japanese word for "continuous improvement", and the kaizen burst symbolizes the need for a continuous improvement project or effort. We will present more details on the kaizen methodology in the next chapter, but suffice it to say here that the burst represents a desired improvement project. Just write an abbreviated description of the improvement idea inside of the kaizen burst symbol. The need for a quality check using the check-do-check method would be documented as shown here.

Following is a description of the most common Lean methods that you will want to use in implementing your process improvements. There is a lot more to know about these methods than can be included here, but luckily there is no shortage of information about them elsewhere.

Standardization. This tool is listed first, since without a standard procedure, even a broken one, there is limited opportunity for improvement. Every process needs to be well defined, documented and deployed. This is not a new requirement for healthcare, obviously, but procedures are not always detailed enough, user-friendly, and deployed properly. For example, the process for disinfecting an OR suite is well defined, but in the rush of the moment the procedure is not always followed correctly. These deficiencies come to light during routine audits, or when you are documenting the process as part of a kaizen event.

As we have discussed previously, assess each block on your Value Stream Map in the light of the process maturity model, and document the need for improvement in standardization where needed.

7S or Organization and Housekeeping. This method is also called 5S, and it refers to a step-by-step process of achieving a high level of organization and housekeeping in a work environment. The expression comes for the use of five or seven words that begin with the letter "S", as a mnemonic technique to remember the steps. The original method included five steps, and we have added two more for good measure, all starting with the letter "S": Sort, Shine, Set in Order, Safety, Security, Standardize, Sustain. When in doubt about what to do for a Lean project, a 7S effort in some area of the OR is a good and safe choice. When reviewing your current state VSM, it would even be useful to assess every process from the 7S perspective. It is rare that an area could not use some improvement in organization and housekeeping.

Quick Changeover. Any time there is an OR suite changeover or turnover, you have the potential for waste. The resource, an OR suite for example, is not available while the changeover is being done. The longer the changeover takes, the higher the waste of this expensive resource. There is a well-defined process for improving changeovers, both in quality and in elapsed time, called Quick Changeover. Originally created for manufacturing, the recommended steps apply equally well to an OR:

1. Separate internal from external steps,
2. Convert internal steps to external steps, and
3. Eliminate waste from all of the remaining steps.

See *Quick Changeover in the OR* for more detail on this important tool.

Supplies Management. The OR is a major consumer of supplies, and also a major storage area for supplies inventory. All too often, however, these supplies are not accounted for precisely, and the dysfunctional par level method is often used. Imagine a bank with millions of dollars in cash, but no strict controls over the disbursements or receipts. Now think of OR supplies as cash, and you have a very similar problem. Fortunately the solutions already exist, and they are not too difficult to implement. The supplies management team needs to be educated in world-class and Lean material management methods, and an overhaul of the supplies management process needs to be high on the to-do list for most hospitals.

Patient Flow. Whenever you have a hand-off of work from one person to another, or from one department to another, you have the very likely possibility of delay and waiting. The reason for this is simple: the receiving department is busy doing something else. You can document inter-departmental hand-offs on your value stream map using a technique called *swim lanes*. Simply organize your process boxes into separate rows on your VSM, with the same department shown on the same row. This technique will give you a visual picture of where the hand-offs across departments happen. Within a department delays can also occur, and these will be obvious by the queue time that existing between steps.

Improving patient flow is a bit like designing a traffic system for cars. Imagine if you had no traffic signs or lights, and cars were expected to make their way across town as best they could. Chaos would ensue. In a Lean work environment we introduce physical signals, called *In Process Kanbans*, to help to manage the work flow in a simple and visual way. These signals can take the form of a flag, a light, a display board, a marked area on the floor, or even an audio signal. These signals control the movement of patients and staff, and just like a traffic system, attempts to avoid a pileup of work.

Check-Do-Check. One simple and low-cost technique that will make a big difference in quality is the method called check-do-check. If a process has the possibility of error, i.e. it is not completely error-proofed, then it is only a matter of time before someone will actually make an error. This is called Murphy's Law: if something can go wrong, it will. If you cannot actually error-proof the process, i.e. make it impossible to do it wrong, then you will need to check your work. It is difficult, however, to check your own work well. After all, you're the one that did it. The check-do-check method asks you to check your own work, and also have your work checked by a co-worker. In that way steps that you might overlook can be caught by a fresh set of eyes. The check-do-check work is built into the standard work defined for that process.

The identification of improvement opportunities is a team effort, gathered around the value stream map, and should be thorough and not rushed. Each opportunity should be documented using the kaizen burst symbol. Following is a small example of how this process might work.

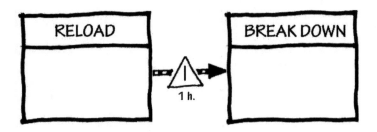

Between the reload and breakdown processes you have documented one hour of wait time, which as you have learned is the waste of waiting. You would like to get the case cart broken down and on its way more quickly in your future state. A solution might be to propose a FIFO (first-in first out) lane or formal incoming aisle for the carts, that would provide a visual signal when work is piling up. If the FIFO lane fills up, that would be a signal for other staff members to come over to help with the breakdown work. Adjusting the size of the FIFO lane would control the amount of waiting time in front of breakdown. Note that this solution would require a change in culture, since the case carts could not simply be pushed into the area if the FIFO lane is full. Staff would need to move to where the work needed to be done, in this example by moving to the breakdown process.

At the end of this session it would not be unusual to have several dozen suggestions documented on the current state VSM. Some of them will be larger projects requiring more than one kaizen event to complete, while other will be simple Just-Do-Its. In the next chapter we'll discuss the steps needed to implement these suggestions. Remember, you haven't actually made any process improvements yet!

Value Stream Map: Completed Current State.

ENZYMATIC FOAM

PRIORITIZE SETS

DECONTAMINATE FLOW

RACK RETURNS

RELOAD		BREAK DOWN		SOAK		MACHINE WASH		COOL DOWN
C/T = 5 MINS.	6 HRS.	C/T = 10 MINS.	2 HRS.	C/T = 4.5 MINS.	2 HRS.	C/T = 55 MINS.	.25 HRS.	C/T = 15 MINS.

| 5 MINS. | 360 MINS. | 10 MINS. | 120 MINS. | 4.5 MINS. | 120 MINS. | 55 MINS. | 15 MINS. | 15 MINS. |

Value Stream Map: Completed Current State.

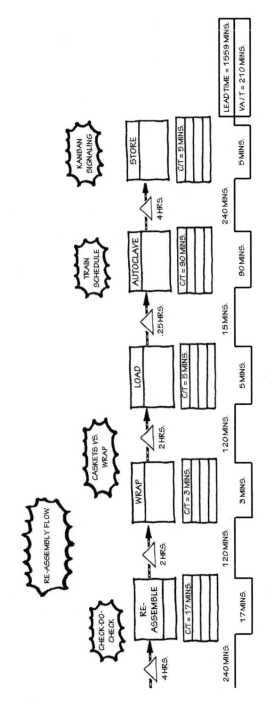

Chapter 10 Knowledge Check

Why is the check-do-check method an important tool in your Lean toolkit?

☐ People don't follow procedures, and they need someone looking over their shoulder to make sure they do a good job.

☐ Even staff members *trying* to do a good job are only human, and having two sets of eyes to check work is sometimes necessary to catch errors.

☐ The check-do-check method can eliminate human errors 100%.

In a kaizen event, what is meant by the term "brainstorming solutions"?

☐ Trying to come up with as many ideas as possible, and not be concerned (yet) about whether they are good or not.

☐ Applying Lean thinking and methods to the sources of waste previously identified, based on best practices.

☐ Relying on some kaizen experts to come up with the ideas that the team can then implement.

True or False: Since no work is being done between processes, there is typically little improvement that can be made in those parts of the value stream.

☐ True
☐ False

Chapter 11: Assign Solutions to Kaizen Events

So far in your journey you have accomplished a lot. You have documented the current state value stream map,  you have identified waste in the process, you have developed some proposed solutions for the elimination of this waste, and you have created a list of kaizen bursts on the VSM. What is missing still is a concrete plan for implementing these improvements and actually accomplishing these benefits. Without this last step, all of the work you have done previously can be considered waste, work that adds time and cost without adding value to the patient.

Kaizen is a Japanese word for "continuous improvement", and the kaizen burst symbolizes the need for a continuous improvement project or effort. A simple project that can be completed by a single person in a short amount of time could be called a *Just Do It* kaizen, where neither a team nor a lot of justification and analysis are needed. Once the *Just Do It* is approved, and approval is a necessary step, the implementation of the suggestion can be done quickly.

Another type of kaizen is the Kaizen Event, a project of three to five days that involves planning and the formation of a kaizen team. Planning for a kaizen event takes more skill, leadership and direction since you are consuming hospital resources, follow-up is more intensive, and the stakes are higher. The management of a database of larger kaizen opportunities is best done by a centralized internal owner who can provide coordination and oversight of projects being conducted in multiple departments. This will often be the Quality department, but many hospitals these days have established an independent organization to direct Lean process improvement projects and training.

Should a centralized Lean department in a hospital actually lead the various kaizen events and projects? Our opinion is no. While cross-department coordination of improvement projects is necessary, the actual kaizen team work should be lead by staff from the affected departments. There are several reasons for this recommendation:

1. Internal staff will know the processes and the details of the work better than outsiders who have not worked in the department.

2. Internal staff will be regarded as "one of us" instead of an outsider.

3. Since an internal staff person will be staying with the department, the opportunity for follow-up and sustainability are higher.

4. Buy-in from the department will be greater and faster if the change is proposed by someone from the department instead of a consultant from the outside.

There is one exception to what we have just stated. We recommend that the team leader for a kaizen event be from outside of the kaizen area. The expectation is that in this way the team leader can be more neutral and with fewer preconceptions about the department work. The team leader will need to have some familiarity with the target area, but does not have the be the #1 expert in the processes being worked on.

Setting the scope of a kaizen event is extremely important. If the scope of what is trying to be accomplished is too ambitious, the kaizen event runs the risk of not competing the work within the number of days assigned. The goal of a kaizen event is to *complete* the process improvement project, including any training, equipment moves, re-writing of procedures and testing of the new process. It will be very disappointing if you get to the end of the week and major portions of the kaizen have not been completed.

It may be possible to err on the side of not being ambitious enough, but that is relatively rare. Once you begin to dig into a value stream, all kinds of challenges come out of the woodwork that you had not planned on originally. It is not unusual for a kaizen event to uncover additional opportunities that will require additional kaizens to complete.

In summary, the scope needs to be ambitious without being overwhelming. A healthy level of stress should be established, and the team leader is responsible for keeping the team on track.

How long should a kaizen event be? That, of course, will depend on what needs to be done to complete a particular improvement, but the typical time-frame is between three and five days. Anything requiring over five days needs to be subdivided into smaller projects. Three days is sufficient for smaller projects. Four days is a very common duration, and as the kaizen goes into day five, you will often see a substantial drop in energy levels and brain power from your team.

Do you need outside help on a kaizen event? That depends on your level of Lean maturity. Some training will be needed on day 1, to review the Lean tools that will be used, like this discussion on value stream mapping. It is also very helpful to have people on the team who have participated in previous events, and have some feel for what needs to be accomplished. It is typical for the perioperative services department and the hospital as a whole to work with outside Lean experts for awhile, in order to get up to speed, but eventually the hospital will need to build up internal resources to become self-sufficient in Lean capabilities.

In this chapter we discussed the need to organize your improvement effort into logical projects called kaizen events. The main advantage of the kaizen approach is the emphasis on a clear deliverable in a short period of time, and the engagement of a cross-functional team to make that happen. We are big fans of this approach to process improvement.

In the next chapter we will introduce a form, the A3 Team Charter, that will help you to put some structure around each kaizen project. This form will also become a building block for a perioperative services department and a hospital master plan for continuous improvement.

Chapter 11 Knowledge Check

If you are overly ambitious in setting your kaizen project goals, you run the risk of:

- ☐ Not completing the project in the time allotted.
- ☐ Stressing out the team.
- ☐ Giving Lean a bad name.
- ☐ All of the above.

True or False: If possible the kaizen event team leader should be someone from outside of the kaizen area.

- ☐ True
- ☐ False

True or False: A Just Do It kaizen project is something that can be done quickly and easily, and does not need approval.

- ☐ True
- ☐ False

Chapter 12: Develop Kaizen Project Plan

Great ideas do not count for much if they are not implemented. At this point you and your team have a list of 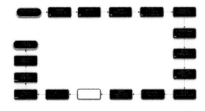 ideas that could address the problems in the value stream and could improve its performance. To change "could" to "will" in the prior sentence you must have a plan: a plan for every idea to become a project and a plan for the value stream to implement all (or the vast majority) of the ideas the team developed so far. The approach we recommend to our clients is to look at each idea individually and to the entire set of idea globally. This will be a bit of an iterative process, as some of the findings from the global view will affect your decisions at the individual project level and vice versa.

Project-by-Project

To convert each improvement idea into a project, we recommend the use of the A3-Team Charter form, as described below. To turn each idea into a project, you must define the following items for each one:

The Issue Statement: This is a short description of the problem you are trying to address. Try to define these issues in terms of actions and facts. Stay away from opinions. Statements like: "Patient hold time in PACU is over 4.2 hours and must be reduced by 50% in 60 days" work better than: "Bad process for picking case carts".

The Target Statement: Write a short paragraph that explains the goal(s) of the project. Be as precise as possible and quantify as much as you can: "Improve case cart accuracy by 60% in 90 days". There is a very good chance that you do not currently track case cart accuracy, and that case cart accuracy is perceived as very low. This may be absolutely correct, but we strongly discourage you from pursuing projects just on the basis of perception. You may have to start measuring case cart accuracy immediately until you reach a significant sample size, and then go back to the project of improving case cart accuracy.

The two items above are normally what is handed to a kaizen team leader to start the project preparation. The next few sections show you how to complete the A3-Team Charter form.

Analysis: Succinctly describe what tools you used to reach the conclusion that this issue deserves a kaizen. You may not have all the information you need to complete this section at the time of the value stream analysis. Normally, this section is completed during the pre-kaizen preparation or during the first few hours of the actual kaizen.

Action Items: Describe the proposed actions for the kaizen team. These are the improvement ideas that the kaizen team developed during the course of the kaizen projects and has decided to implement. Not all ideas proposed during the kaizen event can be implemented and some of them are tabled for later implementation. In this section, describe the ideas that will be implemented within this kaizen event.

Deployment Plan: A simple table with the action items identified to complete the kaizen event with the responsible team member and the expected completion date.

Gantt Chart: Develop a visual timeline with important milestones to aid with project deployment. A simple hand-drawn precedence-style chart or a Gantt chart will suffice for this purpose.

See the example of the A3 Team Charter form on the following page. You can download a copy at the listing for this book at the Flow Publishing website.

All the Value Stream's Projects in One Place

To organize all the projects and have a value stream-wide view of the continuous improvement path, use the A3-X Chart. This chart is a very useful tool to organize your projects, as it displays the correlation among all the different characteristics of a project or set of projects. The basic elements in an A3-X Chart are:

Strategies Section: In this section of the A3-X Chart enter the value stream's key strategic goals.

Lean Hospital
A3 - Team Charter

Team Name: SPD Flow Masters

Project Theme: Total Quality Management

Issue Statement

The quality of the instrument sets arriving to the OR is sub-optimal. Sets some incomplete or not completely clean, or hinged instruments are not properly lubricated. A 4-week study reveals that approximately 22% of the sets have a workmanship related defect of some kind.

Target Statement

To reduce the percentage of defective instrument sets to zero in six months. The first milestone is to reduce it to less than 10% in 30 days.

Action Items

Identify defect types and group in six categories.
Start tracking defects per type.
Create a Pareto chart of defect types.
Identify Self-Check opportunities in Standard Work Definitions.
Identify TQM Checks in SWD.
Develop a plan to implement Check-Do-Check.

Deployment Plan

What	Who	When
Id defect types	Richard	April 17
Defect tracking charts	David	April 24
Pareto spreadsheet	David	April 25
Write SWDs	George	April 28
Acquire GWI software	Kim	May 2
Look for Check-Do-Check opport.	Robin	April 12

Analysis

Gantt Chart

Team Leader:

Date:

Statements like "Have zero surgical site infections" or "Patients will not wait for pre-surgery" or "PACU hold times will be zero" should be in this area. There will be another section for more specific, metric-based goals. See the form below, where this section is comprised of columns on the left-had side of the table.

Projects Section: One of the most valuable outcomes of all the work you and your colleagues have done so far is the list of improvement opportunities. Each of those ideas was converted into a project using the A3-Team Charter form. There is a chance that some of those ideas were consolidated or split, so there will not be a one-to-one correlation between the number of ideas on the list and the number of projects with Team Charters. Each of those A3-Team Charter projects must be included in the Projects section. See the form below, and you can see that the projects are entered as rows on the top of the table.

Metrics Section: In this section enter the value stream's critical process improvement targets in the form of metrics. In this area you should see metrics like PACU hold times, Surgical Site infections, On-time start performance, Supply Shortages, etc. Notice in the provided form that this section is to the center-right of the table.

Team Members Section: In these columns, enter the names of the likely team members that your team considers are good candidates for the kaizen projects.

Financial Results Section: In these rows enter the values of some key financial metrics that reflect the value stream's performance. A project that eliminates waste will have a positive impact on the value stream's financial performance, but it may not be seen on the short term. Do not let yourself be guided only by short-term financial goals. Always remember that your number one priority is to improve quality of care, and all other benefits will follow.

Analyzing Correlations: In the corners of the form, at the intersection of the rows and columns we described above, you can see that you have the opportunity to analyze the relationship of individual pairs. Use a simple scale of Low correlation (▲), Medium correlation (○), and High correlation (●).

- Strategies to Projects: How is each project correlated to each individual strategy?

- Projects to Metrics: How is each project likely to affect each metric?

- Metrics to results: To what degree is a positive impact on each metric likely to result in movement on a financial metric?

- Financial Metrics to Strategies: What is the degree of correlation between each pair of strategy/financial metric?

- Projects to Team Members: Rank the team members according to their expected level of participation on the projects. Use the High correlation symbol to identify a team Leader, a

Medium correlation symbol for a team member and a Low correlation symbol to exclude this person from this particular project.

Lean Hospital — A-3 X Chart

Team Members: PAUL, GEORGE, KIM, ROBIN, NANCY, EDNA, LYNDA

Value Stream Champion: CHARLES BROWN

Instrument Set Re-Processing

Strategies:
- KANBAN SIGNALING
- TRAIN SCHEDULE
- GASKETS VS WRAP
- RE-ASSEMBLY FLOW
- CHECK-DO-CHECK
- RACK RETURNS
- DECONTAM FLOW
- PRIORITIZE SETS
- ENZIMATIC FOAM

Metrics:
- SURGICAL-SITE INFECTIONS
- ON-TIME STARTS
- DEFECTIVE SETS

Results:
- ON-TIME STARTS ABOVE 90%
- ZERO SURGICAL SITE INFECTIONS
- ZERO SURGICAL SUPPLY SHORTAGES
- INVENTORY UNDER $2M
- INCREASE VOLUME BY 20%
- IMPROVE STAFF SAT BY 15 POINTS
- IMPROVE MD SAT BY 25 POINTS
- IMPROVE PATIENT SAT BY 10 POINTS

Correlation Symbols:
- ● Strong Correlation
- ○ Medium Correlation
- ◁ Weak Correlation

See the example below. You can download a copy at the Flow Publishing website.

Project Follow-up

For every completed kaizen project, there has to be some time allowed for the dust to settle and the changes to take hold. During that time, the kaizen team leader must keep an eye on the status of the project and ensure that all the new processes are working as designed while new opportunities for improvement are documented and prioritized for future implementation. At this time is better to not make any more changes, unless they affect the safety of patients or staff. The team leader is expected to report to a coordination body, like a steering committee, at 1 week, 1 month, 3 months, and 6 months from the date of completion. Normally, the project is closed at the 3-month mark. To ensure that the presentations to the steering committee are simple and do not require a great investment of time from the kaizen team leader, we recommend using one more form from the Goal Deployment toolbox, the *Kaizen Status Report* form. The basic elements of the A3 Kaizen Status Report form are:

Background: This is the same as the original Issue Statement, but with the wisdom of hindsight on your side. If the kaizen team or the team leader have no new insights on the original issue, no changes are necessary.

Target Statement: Refer to the Team Charter, as this section has the same content.

Impact: Provide a summary of the general impact of the project on the patients, staff, and other stakeholders. If there is a chart that can quickly communicate the point, e.g. wait time for registration, use it.

New Action Items: Document in this section, any new opportunities for improvement that have become potential projects. Also, any action items identified after the new methods went live are added to this section.

Deployment Plan / Implementation Status: This is the same section you completed for the Team Charter, but we expect that completions will show here. Also display any new projects related to the New Action Items section.

Unresolved Action Items: If there are any overdue Action Items, then show them in this section. The general idea is that the steering committee will look into marshaling the necessary resources to solve these past-due issues.

See the example on the following page. You can download a copy at the Flow Publishing website under this book listing.

Lean Hospital
A3 - Kaizen Status Report
Project Theme: Total Quality Management

LEANHOSPITAL

Team Name: SPD Flow Masters

Background

The quality of the instrument sets arriving to the OR is sub-optimal. Sets some incomplete or not completely clean, or hinged instruments are not properly lubricated. A 4-week study reveals that approximately 22% of the sets have a workmanship related defect of some kind.

New Action Items

Implement 7S in SPD. At times it's hard to find what is needed.
Develop Graphic Work Instructions for set re-assembly.
Evaluate implementation of Instrument Management software.

Target Statement

To reduce the percentage of defective instrument sets to zero in six months. The first milestone is to reduce it to less than 10% in 30 days.

Deployment Plan - Implementation Status

What	Who	When
Id defect types	Richard	April 17 - complete
Defect tracking charts	David	April 24 - complete
Pareto spreadsheet	David	April 25 - complete
Write SWDs	George	April 28 - in progress
Acquire GWI software	Kim	May 2 - pending
Look for Check-Do-Check opport.	Robin	April 12 - in progress

Impact

It was expected that the implementation of TQM techniques, spearheaded by Check-Do-Check, would allow for the reduction in defective sets by 10% in the first month. The last measurements show an improvement of 14%.

Unresolved Action Items

Standard work definitions for the highest users have been completed but many remain to be done for the lower volume sets. Instrument Management software requires intervention from Steering Committee.

Date: June 27, 2002 - 1 month after completion   **Team Leader: Horatio Goicochea**

The three forms above will help you organize and prioritize the many ideas for improvement developed by the Value Stream mapping team. By the end of this phase of the roadmap you and your team will have a very solid sense of what project you want to start first. This may coincide with your initial sense of priorities or you may be surprised by an issue or issues that were not on your radar screen because you do not live with (or suffer...) them every day. Do go into this phase with an open mind, which does not mean to leave behind your common sense. One more thing about prioritizing projects; an OR Nurse told me once that pain is not an absolute measure. Your pain may not be a big deal to me, but it is your pain and what matters is not how I see your pain but the fact that it hurts *you*. Sometimes, being aware of what hurts in your daily life as you work hard to deliver the best possible care to your patients is your best compass to determine what project(s) to go after first.

You and your team should now have a list of projects in order of priority to start working from. The next question is: "What would this value stream look like if you were to implement all the projects on the list?"

Chapter 12 Knowledge Check

The main purpose of the "A3-X chart" is to:

☐ Ensure alignment of vision, activities, results, measurements and people.

☐ To create a database of process improvement projects.

☐ To identify projects that have been completed by "X-ing" them out.

A single A3 Team Charter form is used to plan for every:

☐ Department
☐ Kaizen Event
☐ Individual Staff Member
☐ Value Stream Initiative

On the A3-X chart, if the correlation between a perioperative services department's vision and the planned projects is weak, this is an indication that:

☐ The perioperative services department needs a new vision statement.

☐ The perioperative services department needs to reassess both vision and projects, to ensure a strong correlation.

☐ More improvement projects need to be added to the chart, to increase the possibility of better alignment.

Chapter 13: Draw Future State VSM

By now you and your team have a very good idea of where you want to take this value stream. There is a very good chance that you 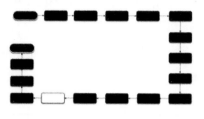 and your team members have a shared vision of the future. This vision was probably reached through discussion, compromise, and consensus. It is important that the vision of the value stream's future is not forced on the team or they will have a hard time supporting it, let alone explaining it to others.

Now you need to find a way to display that vision in a way that is easily understandable and that is founded on the common language you have developed with your team in the OR and across the whole hospital. A very good way to present this vision is by drawing another value stream map that answers the question: "How would the current state value stream map look if all the proposed improvements were to be implemented?" We call this new version the *future state value stream map*.

You and your team worked hard identifying opportunities for improvement and turning those ideas into tangible kaizen projects. Those projects must have a direct impact on the value stream's ability to deliver value faster, with higher quality, and lower costs. Let's analyze a couple of possible projects and their impact on the value stream.

In the current state value stream map, right above the process called Re-Assemble there are three kaizen bursts that seek to improve the quality and speed of the instrument sets. Let's start with the simplest project.

Caskets versus Wrapped Sets: You have all seen them and this sterile processing department has been considering adopting those aluminum cases to replace as many wrapped sets as possible. They realize that not all the wrapping can be eliminated, but they want to move in that direction. The team decided to test wrapping versus closing and they are ready to make a case for the investment in the aluminum cases they refer to as "caskets". The expectation is that this project will reduce the number of punctured wrappers.

Reassembly Flow: In the current state, instrument sets are reassembled in batches, wrapped in batched and then loaded to the autoclave rack in batches. This practice is the reason for instrument sets to pile in between these processes waiting to be worked on by the next process. This project seeks to eliminate the delays in between the processes Re-Assemble, Wrap, and Load. The expected solution is to design a "cell" capable of reassembling, wrapping, and loading one instrument set at a time. By flowing instrument sets, rather than batching them, they will not wait in between processes, effectively eliminating the wait times in between processes. Another benefit expected by the team is that the total processing time through the cell will be 19 minutes, a reduction of 6 minutes over the batch method. This was the result of the team testing the new reassembly process, which includes the aluminum caskets, to see if it was feasible before proposing it as a project.

It must be noted that in many occasions, it is not known with certainty how the project will be carried out. That is OK. You do not have to know everything to conduct a kaizen event. Do bring ideas to the table, but also bring your questions and work with your team to find the solutions.

Check-Do-Check: In more than one occasion, the OR team opened an instrument set to find that it was incomplete, not perfectly clean, the wrapper was punctured, the hinged instruments improperly threaded or any other quality problems. Any of these quality problems may be the result of lack of training, lack of standard work instructions, rushed work, or simple human nature. In the best of environments, humans make mistakes. The key is to not allow human mistakes to become defective instrument sets. One effective tool in fighting human errors is the "check-do-check" technique. This is a technique by which standard work is divided into three sequential elements.

1. Check the quality of the work coming to you. In this case, the tech reassembling the instrument set would check it for completion and cleanliness at a minimum. Different instrument sets may have different quality criteria associated with them. All these difference must be captured in the standard work definitions.

2. You do your own standard work. In this case, the work is to reassemble, or wrap, or load the set to the autoclave's rack.

3. Check the quality of your own work. Before you let go of a set, you must check any quality points determined to be critical by the standard work. This could be the completeness of the set; the location of the instruments in the tray; the order in which the hinged instruments are threaded. The main challenge here is going to be the necessary second set of eyes to check the quality of the outgoing work. One possible solution is to have the instrument techs work in pairs where they check each-other's sets and then proceed to wrap and load.

If you look at just these three projects, they are likely to collapse three processes into one, eliminate four hours of wait time and reduce six minutes of work time. That needs to be displayed in the future state value stream map.

Let's quickly review the other projects.

Enzymatic Foam: The VSM team indicated that one of the reason why the decontamination of instrument sets takes longer than it should is that the OR staff members are not consistent in the use of the enzymatic foam on used sets. A kaizen team will be convened to identify the root causes on this problem and to develop stop gap measures as well as permanent solutions to address the problem.

Prioritize Sets: The SPD team is challenged many times to maintain proper priority on instrument sets, especially those sets which the department does not have too many. This causes late starts as well as a constant stream of phone calls to SPD that at times prevents the SPD team from reaching a smooth operation. A kaizen project will be the vehicle to develop a method of prioritization of instruments sets considering the conditions of "Normal", "Rush", "Stat", and "Stat Flash".

Decontam Flow: This project is the counterpart to the "Reassembly Flow" and all the same considerations apply.

Rack Returns: This issue, as identified by the VSM kaizen team, refers to managing the return of the washer-disinfector racks from the clean side, so they can be loaded on the decontamination side. A kaizen team will calculate the number of necessary racks as well as develop a standardized procedure to control the movement of racks.

Train Schedule: This project will seek to identify the benefits of running the steam autoclaves on full racks or on a fixed schedule.

Kanban Signaling: The SPD team members indicated that signaling is sometimes not clear as to when an instrument set is needed. This kaizen project will seek to implement a kanban system for instrument sets.

The brief description of the projects above is very likely what will be used as the "Issue Statement" or "Target Statement" in the A3-Team Charter forms associated with this value stream mapping project.

Once these projects are implemented to the Instrument Set value stream, they are expected to have an outcome that needs to be predicted by the VSM team. That prediction needs to come in the form of a new value stream map that reflects the impact of those improvement projects. It could look the map shown on the following page.

Value Stream Map: Completed Future State.

LEAD TIME = 355 MINS.	
VA./T=199 MINS.	

What is the likelihood that the future looks exactly like this? Well, it is hard to say. In our experience, the future should be *better* than what the future state VSM shows. It is reasonable to expect that as kaizen projects are completed, many others are being identified and implemented, and more waste than expected would be eliminated, making the value stream much more efficient.

Well, the value stream analysis project is complete. You and your team can relax and pat yourselves on the back for a job well done. There is a very good chance that you feel tired and yet very energized. Now is the time to tell everybody about the project and have them catch the same continuous improvement fever that infected the VSM team. In other words, it is time to put together and deliver a progress report.

Chapter 13 Knowledge Check

How long should it take to achieve the future state shown in the future state value stream map?

- ☐ Less than one year.
- ☐ Between 18 and 24 months.
- ☐ Trick question. The future will always be in the future, and therefore never actually achieved.
- ☐ It depends on the resources applied, the sense of urgency, and what needs to be accomplished.

What performance improvement do you expect to see looking at the timeline at the bottom of your future state VSM?

- ☐ Reductions in labor costs in the value stream.
- ☐ Improvements in quality for key processes.
- ☐ An improvement in the value-add time versus the total elapsed time.

Once the future state VSM has been created, what is the *next step* on the value stream mapping roadmap?

- ☐ Launch your first improvement kaizen events as soon as possible.
- ☐ Host a celebration party with the VSM team.
- ☐ Document the VSM results and present to upper management.

Chapter 14: Present VSM Results

 An important conclusion to any kaizen event, including a value stream mapping project like the one we've been describing, is the final presentation. Lean practitioners sometimes call this a *report-out*. Don't ask me where that expression originated, but we use it.

Activities like a value stream mapping project are consistently successful, most times exceeding your expectations. The report-out is therefore something to look forward to, a chance to share with others what has been accomplished, and even brag a little bit. It is also a unique opportunity for many of your VSM team members to speak in front of senior management. While some will be terrified of this prospect, you'll have a hard time containing the enthusiasm of your team members once they get started.

Standard Elements of the Report-Out

The final report is often done as a PowerPoint presentation, using a standard template created by your hospital. The advantages of using a standard template are a consistent look and feel, a placeholder for each item that needs to be included, and additional notes in the notes section of each slide to guide their completion. Within the presentation you should expect to have the following sections:

- The Team Name, Photo and Team Member Names
- The Kaizen Goals
- Baseline Metrics
- What Was Accomplished, including photos, metrics and short descriptions.
- Surprises, Things You Didn't Expect
- Estimated Benefits
- Any Remaining Action Items

You should plan on a 30-45 minute presentation, and allow time for questions during and after the report-out.

Who Creates the Report?

The kaizen event team leader is the person primarily responsible for the creation of the presentation, although he/she is not responsible for presenting it. We strongly suggest starting ahead of time, and filling in the presentation as the week progresses and data is available. It's not a good feeling (been there) to not have the report done and the scheduled meeting time looming. The presentation itself should be a shared responsibility among the team. Most team members will be up to the challenge, but some may be paralyzed by the thought of having to stand up and talk to an audience. Don't let anyone off the hook, but sometimes having people present in small teams does wonders to reduce the stress level.

Management's Role in the Report-Out

Every effort should be made to have senior management attend the report-out, and a value stream kaizen event is especially important. The master plan for improvement that is the central topic of discussion is something that management needs to understand and lead. Poor attendance by upper management to an event like this sends a signal to the team that the subject is not particularly important.

Management may also need some coaching in their role at the presentation itself. It is simple: thank the participants for their hard work, and express a commitment to getting the suggestions implemented. The report-out is not the time to air objections, to provide a detailed critique of the plan, or to come up with other ideas. Leave those for another time, if at all.

Reporting Results

The results that will be reported at the end of the VSM week are estimates only, since presumably nothing has actually been improved yet. The size of the potential benefit will have a strong influence on which projects are chosen to work on first, with quality being the highest concern followed by financial goals and team-building projects. Your financial estimates should be conservative and easy to understand and explain. Pick a time horizon that is realistic but adequately long. Why report on the savings for only one year, when you expect the improvement to extend to multiple years? Saving $2M over a three-year period sounds better than saving $700K a year, and it is equally true.

Following Up and Next Steps

In a normal department-based kaizen event, follow-up for any remaining action items is the responsibility of the team leader. A value stream mapping kaizen event, presumably extending beyond just one department and generating dozens of improvement suggestions, is slightly different. If there are any short-term action items remaining, these would continue to be the responsibility of the team leader to complete. Execution of the master plan, however, should be passed off to the group directing continuous improvement at the hospital. This could be a dedicated Lean department, a quality department that directs continuous improvement projects, or even a department-level Unit Based Council.

There is a lot more to say about the running of a kaizen event, which we will need to address in another book, *Kaizen in the OR*.

Chapter 14 Knowledge Check

The role of upper management at the VSM final presentation is to:

☐ Provide a detailed critique of the results
☐ Take credit for most of the good ideas
☐ Provide real-time approval of the ideas and launch the implementation effort immediately.
☐ None of the above.

All of the VSM team members should participate in the final presentation, but some team members might be shy. The best way to encourage participation is to:

☐ Have team members present as a small group.
☐ Tell the team member to "grow up".
☐ Offer a small monetary incentive in exchange for speaking.

It is important to create and use a standard template for the final presentation because:

☐ The template provides a checklist of what should be included.
☐ The template provides a design standard for consistency.
☐ The template can include instructions for each slide that other teams can use.
☐ Using a template saves time.
☐ All of the above reasons.

Chapter 15: Epilogue

You've accomplished a lot so far, so let's summarize the tools and plans that have been developed.

1. A current state value stream map.
2. A database of process improvement ideas.
3. A future state value stream map.
4. A master plan for implementation of the suggestions.

Unfortunately, unless you take action to implement your suggestions, all of your work so far will become waste! You don't plan to leave it here, of course, and following are some suggestions for making these improvements a reality.

It's important to keep in mind the prize waiting at the future state. For most hospitals, value stream improvements will result in millions, tens of millions or in some cases hundreds of millions of dollars in savings. Does that sound too extreme? Just add up the total expenditures of the hospital on staff, supplies, utilities, equipment and building. It's a big number. Could you believe that 10% of this expenditure is waste? That would be a conservative estimate. What do those dollars add up to?

You're not going to find these savings in one easy to fix location, however. You're going to need to do the hard work of improving your value streams bit by bit, kaizen by kaizen, because this waste is spread throughout the value stream. Some projects are easier, and we call these the *low-hanging fruit*. Once these are accomplished, though, you'll need to start climbing the trees. The value stream mapping method is a great way to get started. Here are three other critical components:

Top Management Leadership. Transforming a value stream, or many value streams, won't happen by itself or with department-level enthusiasm alone. We have *never* seen a successful Lean endeavor without strong leadership from the top, ideally from the CEO. Let's say it again: we have never seen a sustained Lean initiative with strong leadership from the top.

Pig-Headed Discipline and Determination. Sticking with it is hard, and many hospitals will fall by the wayside. They may accomplish some good things, but without a stick-to-it determination you can't grab the brass ring. W. Edwards Deming, one of the pioneers of Lean thinking, called this constancy *of purpose*. Where does this come from? Look again to your hospital leadership.

Get Up the Learning Curve Fast. If you are looking at a multi-million dollar opportunity, what are you waiting for? You need to get up the learning curve as quickly as possible, and to do that you need a coach or mentor. Remember that even world-class athletes still have a coach. Coaches can be existing hospital employees, or you may need to get some outside help from experienced Lean trainers. Either way, don't waste your time reinventing the wheel.

Best wishes for a successful Lean journey, and we look forward to hearing from you.

Lean Hospital Group

The Lean Hospital Group is an association of like-minded organizations with the mission of promoting Lean principles and tools in hospitals. Leonardo Group Americas is a founding member.

Leonardo Group Americas LLC (LGA)

The authors are the Principals with Leonardo Group Americas, LLC. The mission of *Leonardo Group Americas* is to assist its hospital clients to achieve success with the implementation of advanced Lean methods. This is accomplished through our talented staff and their profound knowledge and experience, a suite of world-class training seminars, state of the art web-based training, certification programs, books and materials, and through the prudent application of Lean software tools.

LGA has been involved with the deployment of Lean in hospitals since 2002, and is a founding member of the Lean Hospital Group. They have conducted Lean improvement projects in virtually every hospital process and Value Stream.

Find out more about Leonardo Group Americas at:

www.leonardogroupamericas.com
www.leanhospitalgroup.com
contact@leonardogroupamericas.com.

Other books in the *In the OR* series are available at www.flowpublishing.com.

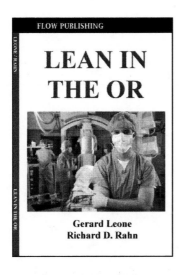

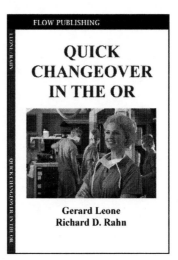